REVISE EDEXCEL GCSE (9–1)
Chemistry
Higher

REVISION WORKBOOK

D0333229

Series Consultant: Harry Smith
Author: Nigel Saunders

A note from the publisher

In order to ensure that this resource offers high-quality support for the associated Pearson qualification, it has been through a review process by the awarding body. This process confirms that this resource fully covers the teaching and learning content of the specification or part of a specification at which it is aimed. It also confirms that it demonstrates an appropriate balance between the development of subject skills, knowledge and understanding, in addition to preparation for assessment.

Endorsement does not cover any guidance on assessment activities or processes (e.g. practice questions or advice on how to answer assessment questions), included in the resource nor does it prescribe any particular approach to the teaching or delivery of a related course.

While the publishers have made every attempt to ensure that advice on the qualification and its assessment is accurate, the official specification and associated assessment guidance materials are the only authoritative source of information and should always be referred to for definitive guidance.

Pearson examiners have not contributed to any sections in this resource relevant to examination papers for which they have responsibility.

Examiners will not use endorsed resources as a source of material for any assessment set by Pearson.

Endorsement of a resource does not mean that the resource is required to achieve this Pearson qualification, nor does it mean that it is the only suitable material available to support the qualification, and any resource lists produced by the awarding body shall include this and other appropriate resources.

Question difficulty

Look at this scale next to each exam-style question. It tells you how difficult the question is.

For the full range of Pearson revision titles across KS2, KS3, GCSE, Functional Skills, AS/A Level and BTEC visit:
www.pearsonschools.co.uk/revise

Pearson

Contents

Edexcel publishes Sample Assessment Material and the Specification on its website. This is the official content and this book should be used in conjunction with it. The questions have been written to help you practise every topic in the book. Remember: the real exam questions may not look like this.

Formulae

1 Which of the following is the formula for calcium carbonate?

☐ **A** $CaCO$

☐ **B** $CaCO_2$

> Put a cross in **one** box. Always answer multiple-choice questions, even if you don't actually know the answer.

☐ **C** $CaCO_3$

☐ **D** $CaCO_4$ **(1 mark)**

2 State what is meant by the term **element**.

An element is a substance made from ....

with the same number of .... **(2 marks)**

3 Chlorine is used to kill harmful microorganisms in drinking water. Its formula is Cl_2.

(a) Explain, using the information given, how you know that chlorine is **not** a compound.

....

....

.... **(2 marks)**

(b) Explain, using the information given, how you can tell that chlorine exists as molecules.

....

....

.... **(2 marks)**

4 Complete the table to show the formulae of some common substances.

Substance	water	carbon dioxide	methane	sulfuric acid	sodium
Formula					

(5 marks)

5 The formula for aluminium hydroxide is $Al(OH)_3$.

(a) State the number of elements in the formula $Al(OH)_3$.

.... **(1 mark)**

(b) State the total number of atoms in the formula $Al(OH)_3$.

.... **(1 mark)**

6 The formula for a carbonate ion is CO_3^{2-}. Describe what this formula shows.

....

.... **(2 marks)**

Equations

1 Which of these statements describes a chemical reaction?

☐ **A** Reactants form from products.

☐ **B** Products form from reactants.

☐ **C** An element changes into another element.

☐ **D** The total mass of substances goes down.

> Answer **C** cannot be correct because one element cannot change to another element in chemical reactions.

(1 mark)

2 Sodium hydroxide solution reacts with dilute hydrochloric acid to form sodium chloride and water.

(a) Write the word equation for this reaction.

.... **(1 mark)**

(b) Write the balanced equation for this reaction.

.... **(1 mark)**

3 A teacher adds a piece of sodium metal to some water. The reaction produces sodium hydroxide solution and bubbles of hydrogen.

> You should know the formulae of elements and simple compounds.

> **Guided**

(a) Complete the balanced equation below to show the correct state symbols.

$2Na(......) + 2H_2O(......) \rightarrow 2NaOH(......) + H_2(......)$ .... **(1 mark)**

(b) Describe how you know that the equation above is balanced.

....

.... **(2 marks)**

4 The following equations are **not** balanced. Write the balanced equations in the spaces below them.

> Do not add state symbols unless you are asked for them.

(a) $Cu + O_2 \rightarrow CuO$

.... **(1 mark)**

(b) $Al + Fe_2O_3 \rightarrow Al_2O_3 + Fe$

.... **(1 mark)**

(c) $Mg + HNO_3 \rightarrow Mg(NO_3)_2 + H_2$

.... **(1 mark)**

(d) $Na_2CO_3 + HCl \rightarrow NaCl + H_2O + CO_2$

.... **(1 mark)**

(e) $Fe + O_2 \rightarrow Fe_2O_3$

.... **(1 mark)**

(f) $Cl_2 + NaBr \rightarrow NaCl + Br_2$

.... **(1 mark)**

Ionic equations

1   Explain what is meant by the term **ion**.

Guided

An ion is a ....

formed when .... **(2 marks)**

2   Silver nitrate solution is used to identify iodide ions in solution. A yellow precipitate of silver iodide, AgI, forms if iodide ions are present.

(a) Give the formula of the silver ion and the formula of the iodide ion in silver iodide.

silver ion ....

iodide ion .... **(2 marks)**

(b) Write the balanced ionic equation for the formation of silver iodide. Include state symbols.

.... **(2 marks)**

3   Dilute acids contain hydrogen ions. These react with carbonate ions to form water and carbon dioxide.

(a) Give the formula for a hydrogen ion and the formula for a carbonate ion.

hydrogen ion ....

carbonate ion.. **(2 marks)**

(b) Write the balanced ionic equation for the reaction described above.

.... **(2 marks)**

4   The following ionic equations are **not** balanced. Write the balanced equations in the spaces below them.

(a) $Fe^{2+} + OH^- \rightarrow Fe(OH)_2$

.... **(1 mark)**

(b) $Fe^{3+} + OH^- \rightarrow Fe(OH)_3$

.... **(1 mark)**

5   Alkaline solutions contain hydroxide ions. These react with hydrogen ions during neutralisation reactions.

(a) Write the ionic equation for the reaction between a hydrogen ion and a hydroxide ion.

.... **(1 mark)**

(b) Name the product of this reaction.

.... **(1 mark)**

6   When chlorine reacts with potassium bromide solution, potassium chloride solution and bromine form:

$Cl_2 + 2KBr \rightarrow 2KCl + Br_2$

> Potassium ions are **spectator ions** in this reaction. They are unchanged and can be left out of the equation.

(a) Write the formulae of all the ions present in this reaction.

.... **(3 marks)**

(b) Write a balanced ionic equation for the reaction.

.... **(2 marks)**

Hazards, risk and precautions

Guided

1 Describe what is meant by the term **hazard**.

A hazard is something that could cause ....

....

.... **(2 marks)**

2 Describe what is meant by the term **risk**.

> **Practical skills** Risk and hazard are **not** the same thing.

....

.... **(2 marks)**

3 Hazard symbols are found on containers. Give **two** reasons why these hazard symbols are used.

....

....

.... **(2 marks)**

Guided

4 Complete the diagram below using a straight line to connect each hazard symbol to its correct description.

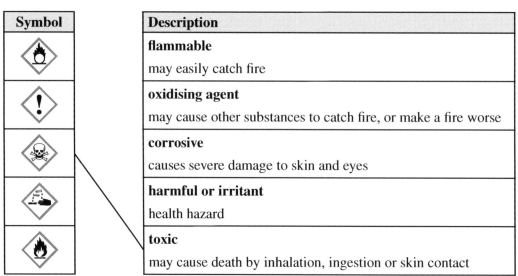

Symbol	Description
	flammable may easily catch fire
	oxidising agent may cause other substances to catch fire, or make a fire worse
	corrosive causes severe damage to skin and eyes
	harmful or irritant health hazard
	toxic may cause death by inhalation, ingestion or skin contact

(4 marks)

5 Copper reacts with concentrated nitric acid. The reaction forms copper nitrate, water and nitrogen dioxide. Nitrogen dioxide is a toxic brown gas with an irritating odour.

Explain a suitable precaution, other than eye protection, needed for safe working in this experiment.

....

....

.... **(2 marks)**

Atomic structure

1 Which of these statements correctly describes an atom?

☐ **A** Most of the mass is concentrated in the nucleus.

☐ **B** Most of the charge is concentrated in the nucleus.

☐ **C** The number of neutrons always equals the number of protons.

☐ **D** The number of electrons always equals the number of neutrons. **(1 mark)**

2 Complete the table to show the relative mass, relative charge and position of each particle in an atom.

Particle	proton	neutron	electron
Relative mass		1	
Relative charge			−1
Position	nucleus		

(3 marks)

3 Explain why a hydrogen atom has no overall charge, even though it contains electrically charged particles.

....

.... **(2 marks)**

4 John Dalton described his atomic model of the atom in 1803. Suggest a reason that explains why his model did not include protons, neutrons and electrons.

.... **(1 mark)**

5 The diameter of a gold atom is 2.70×10^{-10} m. The diameter of a gold nucleus is 1.03×10^{-14} m. Calculate, to three significant figures, the diameter of a gold atom relative to the diameter of its nucleus.

> **Maths skills** 1.03×10^{-14} is written in standard form. You could enter it on your calculator as: 1.03 EXP −14.

.... **(2 marks)**

6 Experiments were carried out in the early part of the last century to test the 'plum pudding' model of the atom. A very large number of positively charged particles were fired at a very thin gold sheet.

(a) Suggest a reason that explains why most of these particles passed straight through the gold sheet.

.... **(1 mark)**

(b) The positively charged particles are repelled when they come close to the nucleus of a gold atom. Explain what property of the nucleus is shown by this observation.

....

.... **(2 marks)**

(c) In the experiments, only about 1 in 20 000 positively charged particles was repelled. Explain this observation.

> You may be asked to analyse information and draw conclusions using your knowledge and understanding.

....

.... **(2 marks)**

Isotopes

1 State what is meant by the **mass number** of an atom.

Guided

The mass number of an atom is the total number of ....

.... **(1 mark)**

2 An atom of an element X has an atomic number 9 and a mass number 19. How many electrons does an atom of element X contain?

☐ **A** 9   ☐ **B** 10   ☐ **C** 19   ☐ **D** 28 **(1 mark)**

3 Describe, in terms of particles in the atom, what an element is.

....

....

| What is the same for atoms of a given element, and what is different between atoms of different elements? |

.... **(2 marks)**

4 Hydrogen has three natural isotopes: ^1_1H (hydrogen-1), ^2_1H (hydrogen-2) and ^3_1H (hydrogen-3).

(a) Complete the table to show the numbers of protons, neutrons and electrons in an atom of each isotope.

Isotope	Protons	Neutrons	Electrons
hydrogen-1			
hydrogen-2			
hydrogen-3			

(3 marks)

(b) Explain, in terms of particles, why these are isotopes of the same element.

....

.... **(2 marks)**

5 Explain why relative atomic masses of some elements are whole numbers, but those of some other elements, for example chlorine, are not.

....

....

.... **(2 marks)**

6 A sample of neon contains two isotopes, Ne (neon-20) and Ne (neon-22).

Guided

The relative abundance of neon-20 is 90.5%.

Calculate the relative atomic mass, A_r, of this sample of neon. Give your answer to one decimal place.

relative abundance of neon-22 = (100 – 90.5) = ...

mass of 100 atoms = ...

A_r of Ne = ... **(3 marks)**

Mendeleev's table

1 (a) How did Mendeleev **first start** to arrange the elements in his periodic table?

☐ **A** in the order of increasing number of protons in the nucleus

☐ **B** in the order of increasing reactivity with other elements

☐ **C** in the order of increasing number of isotopes

☐ **D** in the order of increasing relative atomic mass   **(1 mark)**

(b) State **one** factor, other than the one in your answer to part (**a**), that Mendeleev used when he arranged the elements.

.... **(1 mark)**

2 The diagram shows part of Mendeleev's 1871 table.

(a) Give **two** similarities between this table and the modern periodic table.

> Remember that you will be given a periodic table in the exam. There is also one at the back of this book.

			Group			
1	2	3	4	5	6	7
H						
Li	Be	B	C	N	O	F
Na	Mg	Al	Si	P	S	Cl
K	Ca	*	Ti	V	Cr	Mn
Cu	Zn	*	*	As	Se	Br
Rb	Sr	Y	Zr	Nb	Mo	*
Ag	Cd	In	Sn	Sb	Te	I

1 ....

2 ....

(2 marks)

(b) Give **three** differences between this table and the modern periodic table.

1 ....

2 ....

3 .... **(3 marks)**

3 Mendeleev had difficulty placing some elements. For example, the order of tellurium Te and iodine I appeared to be reversed in his table.

(a) Explain why the positions of these two elements appeared to be reversed in Mendeleev's table.

....

....

.... **(2 marks)**

(b) Explain, in terms of atomic structure, why the positions of these two elements were actually correct.

....

....

.... **(2 marks)**

4 State **one** feature of Mendeleev's work with his table that would later help to support his ideas.

.... **(1 mark)**

The periodic table

1 How are the elements arranged in the modern periodic table?

☐ **A** in the order of increasing mass number

☐ **B** in the order of increasing atomic number

☐ **C** in the order of increasing nucleon number

☐ **D** in the order of increasing numbers of electron shells **(1 mark)**

2 The positions of five elements (**A**, **B**, **C**, **D** and **E**) are shown in the periodic table on the right. These letters are **not** the chemical symbols for these elements.

(a) Give the letters of **two** elements that have similar chemical properties to each other.

.... **(1 mark)**

(b) Give the letters of **all** the metal elements.

.... **(1 mark)**

(c) Give the letters of **two** elements in the same period.

.... **(1 mark)**

3 The meaning of the term **atomic number** has changed over time.

> **Guided**

(a) Explain the meaning of the term **atomic number** as Mendeleev might have understood it in the nineteenth century.

The position of ....

.... **(2 marks)**

(b) Explain the modern meaning of the term **atomic number**.

....

.... **(2 marks)**

(c) Suggest a reason that explains why the meaning of atomic number has changed over time.

....

.... **(1 mark)**

4 Sodium is placed between elements **A** and **B** on the periodic table shown in question **2**. Argon is placed immediately above element **E**. Explain why there can only be six elements between sodium and argon.

> Think about why two different elements cannot occupy the same position on the modern periodic table.

....

....

.... **(2 marks)**

Electronic configurations

1　The diagram shows a lithium atom. It is not drawn to scale.

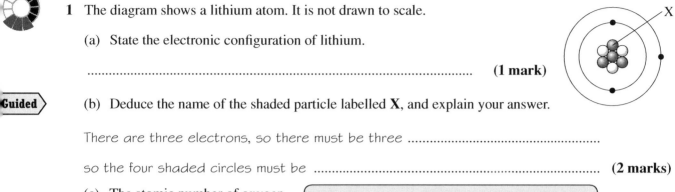

(a)　State the electronic configuration of lithium.

.... **(1 mark)**

Guided

(b)　Deduce the name of the shaded particle labelled **X**, and explain your answer.

There are three electrons, so there must be three ....

so the four shaded circles must be .... **(2 marks)**

(c)　The atomic number of oxygen is 8.

> You need to show each electron shell and electron, but you can show the nucleus as a single dot.

Draw a diagram to show the arrangement of electrons in an oxygen atom.

(2 marks)

2　The table shows some information about two non-metal elements, fluorine and chlorine.

Non-metal element	Atomic number	Electronic configuration
F	9	2.7
Cl	17	2.8.7

(a)　Explain, in terms of electronic configurations, why fluorine and chlorine are placed in group 7.

....

.... **(2 marks)**

(b)　Explain, in terms of electronic configurations, why fluorine and chlorine are **not** in the same period.

....

.... **(2 marks)**

3　Deduce the electronic configurations of the following elements.

(a)　calcium (atomic number 20):

.... **(1 mark)**

(b)　phosphorus (atomic number 15):

.... **(1 mark)**

4　State and explain the number of the group in which helium (electronic configuration 2) is placed.

....

.... **(2 marks)**

Ions

1 Which of the following statements correctly describes the formation of an ion?

☐ **A** Positively charged ions, called cations, form when atoms or groups of atoms gain electrons.

> You can quickly narrow the alternatives if you know the correct name for each type of ion, or how it forms.

☐ **B** Positively charged ions, called anions, form when atoms or groups of atoms lose electrons.

☐ **C** Negatively charged ions, called cations, form when atoms or groups of atoms lose electrons.

☐ **D** Negatively charged ions, called anions, form when atoms or groups of atoms gain electrons.

(1 mark)

2 The atomic number of magnesium, Mg, is 12. The symbol for a magnesium ion is Mg^{2+}.

(a) Deduce the number of electrons in a magnesium ion.

> **Maths skills** Work out the number of electrons in an atom, then add or subtract electrons according to the charge shown.

.... **(1 mark)**

(b) Write the electronic configuration for a magnesium ion.

.... **(1 mark)**

3 Complete the table to show the numbers of protons, neutrons and electrons in each ion.

Ion	Atomic number	Mass number	Protons	Neutrons	Electrons
N^{3-}	7	15	7	8	10
K^+	19	40			
Ca^{2+}	20	40			
S^{2-}	16	32			
Br^-	35	81			

(4 marks)

4 The diagram on the right shows the formation of a sodium ion, Na^+, from a sodium atom.

Draw a similar diagram to show the formation of a chloride ion, Cl^-, from a chlorine atom.

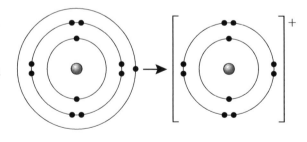

(3 marks)

Formulae of ionic compounds

1   The formula of a sodium ion is Na⁺. The formula of a phosphate ion is PO_4^{3-}. Which of the following is the formula for sodium phosphate?

☐ **A** $NaPO_4$ ☐ **C** Na_2PO_4

☐ **B** $Na(PO_4)_3$ ☐ **D** Na_3PO_4 **(1 mark)**

2   Complete the table to show the formulae of the compounds produced by each pair of ions.

Guided

 You may need more than one of each ion to obtain equal numbers of positive and negative charges.

You need to know the formulae of common ions. This helps you work out the formulae of ionic substances.

	Cl⁻	S²⁻	OH⁻	NO₃⁻	SO₄²⁻
K⁺				KNO₃	
Ca²⁺			Ca(OH)₂		CaSO₄
Fe³⁺		Fe₂S₃			
NH₄⁺	NH₄Cl				

(15 marks)

3   Magnesium ribbon burns in air. It reacts with oxygen to produce magnesium oxide, MgO.

(a) Write the balanced equation for the reaction.

.... **(2 marks)**

(b) Magnesium nitride is also formed, as some of the hot magnesium reacts with nitrogen in the air.

(i)   Nitrogen is in group 5. Suggest reasons that explain why the formula for a nitride ion is N^{3-}.

....

.... **(2 marks)**

(ii) Write the formula for magnesium nitride.

The formula for a magnesium ion is Mg²⁺.

.... **(1 marks)**

(iii) Explain why the NO₃⁻ ion is called the nitrate ion, but the N^{3-} ion is called the nitride ion.

....

.... **(2 marks)**

4   Complete the table to show the names of the ions.

Remember to use the endings –ide and –ate correctly.

	S²⁻	SO₄²⁻	Cl⁻	ClO₃⁻
Name				

(4 marks)

Properties of ionic compounds

1   Which statement about the formation of ionic compounds, such as sodium chloride, is correct?

☐ **A**   Electrons are transferred from metal atoms to non-metal atoms, producing cations and anions.

☐ **B**   Electrons are transferred from cations to anions, producing metal atoms and non-metal atoms.

☐ **C**   Electrons are shared between metal atoms and non-metal atoms.

☐ **D**   Electrons are shared between cations and anions.   **(1 mark)**

2   Ionic compounds have a lattice structure.

(a)   Complete the diagram, using the symbols + and –, to show the positions of positive and negative ions in an ionic lattice.

> **Maths skills**   Remember that opposite charges will attract each other, and like charges will repel.

> You should be able to visualise and represent 2D and 3D forms, including 2D representations of 3D objects.

(1 mark)

(b)   Describe what ionic bonds are.

....

....   **(2 marks)**

3   (a)   Explain why ionic compounds have high boiling points.

> Mention the forces between the particles found in ionic compounds.

....

....   **(2 marks)**

(b)   Suggest a reason that explains why the melting point of MgO is higher than the melting point of NaCl.

....   **(1 mark)**

4   Calcium metal can be produced on an industrial scale by passing an electric current through molten calcium chloride.

> **Guided**

(a)   Explain why molten calcium chloride can conduct electricity.

When calcium chloride is a liquid, its ions are ....

....   **(2 marks)**

(b)   State why solid calcium chloride **cannot** conduct electricity.

....   **(1 mark)**

(c)   Describe one way, other than by melting it, of making calcium chloride conduct electricity.

....   **(1 mark)**

Covalent bonds

1 What are the typical sizes of atoms and small molecules?

Maths skills The quantities are shown in standard form. For example, 10^{-3} is greater than 10^{-6}.

	☐ A	☐ B	☐ C	☐ D
Atoms	10^{-10} m	10^{-10} m	10^{-9} m	10^{-12} m
Molecules	10^{-11} m	10^{-9} m	10^{-12} m	10^{-9} m

(1 mark)

2 Explain how a covalent bond forms.

....

.... **(2 marks)**

3 Hydrogen reacts with fluorine to form hydrogen fluoride: $H_2 + F_2 \rightarrow 2HF$

The electronic configuration of hydrogen is 1 and the electronic configuration of fluorine is 2.7.

Guided

(a) Explain why fluorine atoms can form only one covalent bond.

A fluorine atom has one unpaired electron in its ....

so it .... **(2 marks)**

(b) Describe what the structure, H–H, tells you about a hydrogen molecule.

....

.... **(2 marks)**

(c) Draw the dot-and-cross diagrams for a molecule of each of the following substances, showing the outer electrons only.

> Show each chemical symbol. Show one atom's electrons as dots and the other atom's electrons as crosses.

(i) fluorine:

(2 marks)

(ii) hydrogen fluoride:

(2 marks)

4 The electronic configuration of nitrogen is 2.5.

(a) Draw a dot-and-cross diagram for a nitrogen molecule, N_2. Show the outer electrons only.

(2 marks)

(b) Draw the structure for a nitrogen molecule.

> Look at question **3b**.

.... **(1 mark)**

13

Simple molecular substances

1   Carbon dioxide, CO_2, is found in the air. Why does it have a low boiling point?

   ☐ **A**   There are weak forces of attraction between carbon atoms and oxygen atoms.

   ☐ **B**   There are weak covalent bonds between carbon atoms and oxygen atoms.

   ☐ **C**   There are weak forces of attraction between carbon dioxide molecules.

   ☐ **D**   There are weak covalent bonds between carbon dioxide molecules.   **(1 mark)**

2   The table shows the properties of three different substances (**A**, **B** and **C**).

Substance	Melting point (°C)	Solubility in water (g per 100 g of water)	Conducts electricity when solid?	Conducts electricity when liquid?
A	290	43	no	yes
B	−95	0.001	no	no
C	660	0	yes	yes

State and explain which substance (**A**, **B** or **C**) is a simple molecular substance.

   ....

   ....

   ....   **(3 marks)**

3   Sulfur hexafluoride, SF_6, exists as simple molecules. It is used as an insulating gas for electrical equipment.

   (a)   Explain why sulfur hexafluoride does not conduct electricity.

   > Think about whether simple molecules are electrically charged or contain electrons that are free to move.

   ....

   ....   **(2 marks)**

(b)   Suggest reasons that explain why sulfur hexafluoride does not dissolve in water.

   The intermolecular forces between ....

   are weaker than those between ....

   and those between ....   **(3 marks)**

4   The graph shows the boiling points of three alcohols. Their relative formula masses are shown on each bar.

   Describe the relationship shown by the graph, and suggest a reason that explains it.

   ....

   ....

   ....   **(2 marks)**

Giant molecular substances

1 Silica, SiO_2, does not conduct electricity or dissolve in water. Its melting point is very high.

Which statement describes a molecule of silica?

☐ **A** a giant molecule with ionic bonds

☐ **B** a giant molecule with covalent bonds

☐ **C** a simple molecule with covalent bonds

☐ **D** a simple molecule with ionic bonds

(1 mark)

2 The diagrams below show the structures of diamond and graphite.

> You should be able to visualise and represent 2D and 3D forms, including 2D representations of 3D objects.

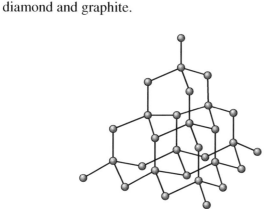

diamond

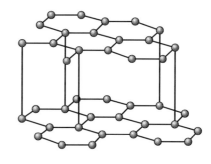

graphite

(a) Name the element that has atoms represented by the balls in the diagrams.

.... **(1 mark)**

(b) State the maximum number of bonds present between each atom in a molecule of diamond.

.... **(1 mark)**

(c) Name the type of structure shown in both diagrams.

.... **(1 mark)**

3 Refer to structure and bonding in your answers to the following questions.

> You need to explain why diamond is very hard.

(a) Explain why diamond is suitable for use in cutting tools.

....

.... **(3 marks)**

Guided (b) Explain why graphite is suitable for use as a lubricant.

The layers in graphite can ....

because .... **(2 marks)**

(c) Explain why graphite is used to make electrodes.

> You need to explain why graphite can conduct electricity.

....

....

.... **(2 marks)**

Other large molecules

1 Ethene, C_2H_4, can be made into a polymer. What is the name of this polymer?

☐ **A** plastic

☐ **B** poly(ethane)

☐ **C** poly(ethene)

☐ **D** poly(ethyne) **(1 mark)**

2 The diagram is a model of a section of a simple polymer.

(a) Name the element with atoms represented by the larger, dark-grey balls in the diagram.

.... **(1 mark)**

(b) Name the type of bonding present in a molecule of this polymer.

.... **(1 mark)**

3 Graphene is a form of carbon. It is a good conductor of electricity and has a very high melting point.

The diagram is a model of part of the structure of graphene.

Guided (a) Explain, in terms of its structure and bonding, why graphene has a very high melting point.

> Include the type of bonds that must be broken during melting.

Graphene has .... bonds in a ....

structure, and these bonds are.. **(3 marks)**

(b) Explain why graphene is a good conductor of electricity.

> Graphene has a structure similar to a layer of graphite.

....

....

.... **(2 marks)**

4 Fullerenes are forms of carbon that include hollow balls, such as buckminsterfullerene, C_{60}.

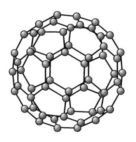

Explain, in terms of bonding, why buckminsterfullerene has a much lower melting point than graphite.

....

....

.... **(3 marks)**

Metals

1 Metal elements and non-metal elements have different typical properties.

Complete the table below by placing a tick (✓) in each correct box.

	Low melting points	High melting points	Good conductors of electricity	Poor conductors of electricity
Metals				
Non-metals				

(4 marks)

2 Most metals are shiny solids with high densities. Explain what having a 'high density' means.

....

.... **(2 marks)**

3 Copper is a metal used in electricity cables. It is a good conductor of electricity and is malleable (it will bend without shattering). The diagram is a model for the structure of copper. Each circle is a copper ion.

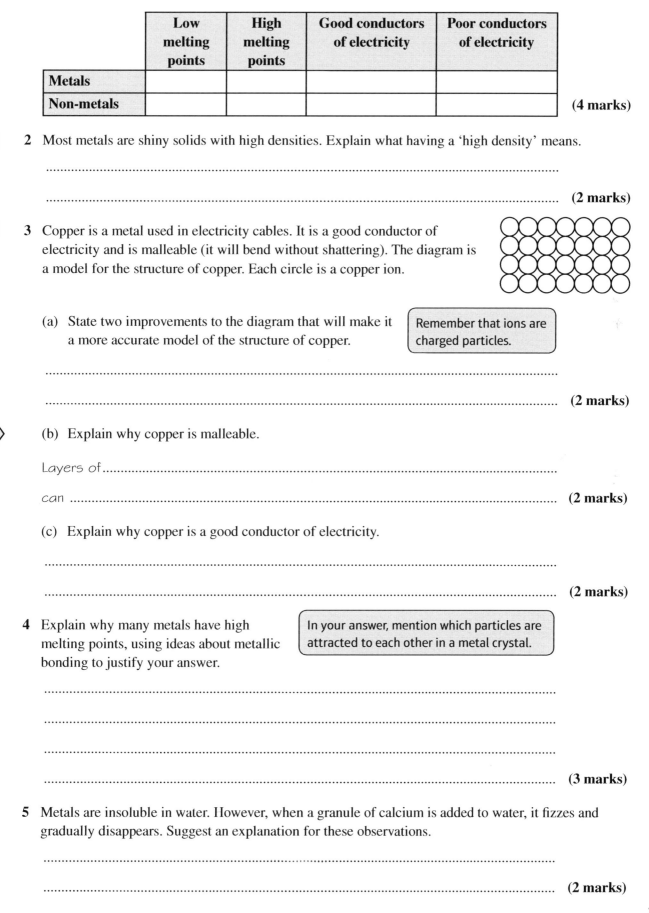

(a) State two improvements to the diagram that will make it a more accurate model of the structure of copper.

Remember that ions are charged particles.

....

.... **(2 marks)**

Guided (b) Explain why copper is malleable.

Layers of ....

can .... **(2 marks)**

(c) Explain why copper is a good conductor of electricity.

....

.... **(2 marks)**

4 Explain why many metals have high melting points, using ideas about metallic bonding to justify your answer.

In your answer, mention which particles are attracted to each other in a metal crystal.

....

....

....

.... **(3 marks)**

5 Metals are insoluble in water. However, when a granule of calcium is added to water, it fizzes and gradually disappears. Suggest an explanation for these observations.

....

.... **(2 marks)**

Had a go ☐ Nearly there ☐ Nailed it! ☐

Limitations of models

1 The formula of a substance can be given in different ways.

Which row (**A**, **B**, **C** or **D**) correctly shows the different formulae for ethene?

		Molecular formula	Empirical formula	Structural formula
☐	**A**	C_2H_6	CH_3	CH_3CH_3
☐	**B**	C_2H_4	CH_2	$CH_2{=}CH_2$
☐	**C**	CH_2	C_2H_4	$CH_2{=}CH_2$
☐	**D**	$CH_2{=}CH_2$	C_2H_4	CH_2

Answer **A** cannot be correct because it describes ethane, not ethene.

(1 mark)

2 The diagrams (**A**, **B**, **C** and **D**) show four different models for a molecule of methane, CH_4.

A	B	C	D
H—C—H with H above and H below	Dot-and-cross diagram of CH₄	Ball-and-stick model	Space-filling model
Structure	**Dot-and-cross diagram**	**Ball-and-stick model**	**Space-filling model**

State the letters (**A**, **B**, **C** or **D**) for the models that:

(a) show the covalent bonds present in a methane molecule

You may need to identify more than one model in your answers.

.... **(1 mark)**

(b) identify the elements present in a methane molecule

.... **(1 mark)**

(c) represent the three-dimensional shape of a methane molecule

.... **(1 mark)**

(d) show the electrons involved in bonding

.... **(1 mark)**

(e) show the relative sizes of each atom in a methane molecule

.... **(1 mark)**

3 A student draws a dot-and-cross diagram of a water molecule. Compare and contrast the advantages and disadvantages of drawing a ball-and-stick model instead.

Think about the limitations of each model. You do not need to write a conclusion in your answer.

....

....

....

.... **(3 marks)**

Relative formula mass

Use the relative atomic masses, A_r, in the table below when you answer the questions.

Element	Al	Ca	Cl	Cu	H	N	O	S
A_r	27	40	35.5	63.5	1	14	16	32

1 Calculate the relative formula mass, M_r, of each of the following substances.

> You do not need to show your working out, but it will help you to check the accuracy of your answers.

> If relative atomic masses are not given in the question, you can find them in the periodic table.

(a) water, H_2O

.... **(1 mark)**

(b) sulfur dioxide, SO_2

.... **(1 mark)**

(c) aluminium oxide, Al_2O_3

.... **(1 mark)**

(d) ammonium chloride, NH_4Cl > Do not round the answer to this question to a whole number.

.... **(1 mark)**

(e) calcium chloride, $CaCl_2$

.... **(1 mark)**

(f) aluminium chloride, $AlCl_3$

.... **(1 mark)**

2 Calculate the relative formula mass, M_r, of each of the following substances.

Guided

(a) calcium hydroxide, $Ca(OH)_2$

$16 + 1 = 17, 17 \times 2 = 34, 40 + 34 =.$ .... **(1 mark)**

(b) aluminium hydroxide, $Al(OH)_3$ > **Maths skills** You could also enter the calculation into your calculator as: $40 + (2 \times (16 + 1)) =$

.... **(1 mark)**

(c) calcium nitrate, $Ca(NO_3)_2$

.... **(1 mark)**

(d) ammonium sulfate, $(NH_4)_2SO_4$

.... **(1 mark)**

(e) aluminium sulfate, $Al_2(SO_4)_3$

.... **(1 mark)**

Practical skills **Empirical formulae**

1 A student carries out an experiment to determine the empirical formula of magnesium oxide. He heats a piece of magnesium ribbon in a crucible. He continues until the contents of the crucible stop glowing.

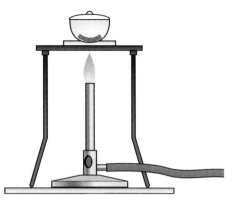

The table shows his results.

Object	Mass (g)
empty crucible and lid	20.24
crucible, lid and contents before heating	20.49
crucible, lid and contents after heating	20.65

(a) Suggest a reason that explains why the student continued heating until the contents stopped glowing.

.... **(1 mark)**

(b) The hot crucible is a hazard. Explain one precaution needed to control the risk of harm.

....

.... **(2 marks)**

Guided

(c) Calculate the empirical formula of magnesium oxide using the student's results.

(A_r of Mg = 24 and A_r of O = 16)

mass of magnesium used = 20.49 g – 20.24 g = 0.25 g

mass of oxygen reacted = 20.65 g – 20.49 g = ...

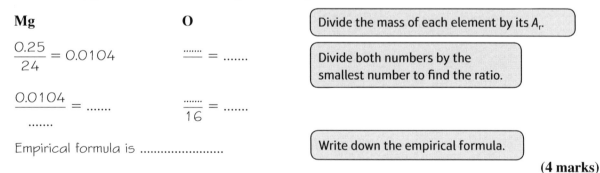

Mg   **O**

$\dfrac{0.25}{24} = 0.0104$ $\dfrac{.......}{.......} = ...$

> Divide the mass of each element by its A_r.

> Divide both numbers by the smallest number to find the ratio.

$\dfrac{0.0104}{.......} = ...$ $\dfrac{.......}{16} = ...$

Empirical formula is ....

> Write down the empirical formula.

(4 marks)

2 In an experiment, 11.2 g of hot iron reacts with 21.3 g of chlorine gas to form iron chloride.

Calculate the empirical formula of the iron chloride.

(A_r of Fe = 56 and A_r of Cl = 35.5)

.... **(2 marks)**

3 The empirical formula of a sample of gas is NO_2. Its relative formula mass, M_r, is 92.

Deduce the molecular formula of the gas.

....

.... **(2 marks)**

Conservation of mass

1   Sodium chloride solution reacts with silver nitrate solution.
Sodium nitrate solution and a white precipitate of solid silver
chloride form: $NaCl(aq) + AgNO_3(aq) \rightarrow NaNO_3(aq) + AgCl(s)$

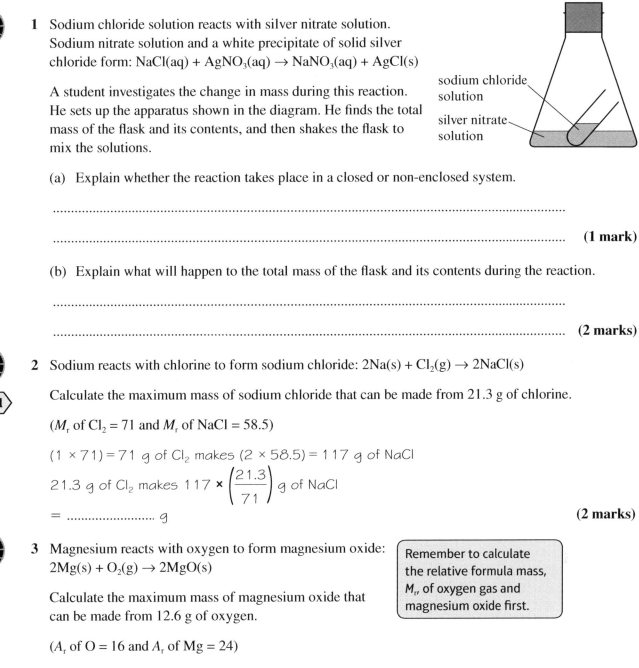

sodium chloride
solution

silver nitrate
solution

A student investigates the change in mass during this reaction.
He sets up the apparatus shown in the diagram. He finds the total
mass of the flask and its contents, and then shakes the flask to
mix the solutions.

(a)   Explain whether the reaction takes place in a closed or non-enclosed system.

....

.... **(1 mark)**

(b)   Explain what will happen to the total mass of the flask and its contents during the reaction.

....

.... **(2 marks)**

2   Sodium reacts with chlorine to form sodium chloride: $2Na(s) + Cl_2(g) \rightarrow 2NaCl(s)$

> Guided

Calculate the maximum mass of sodium chloride that can be made from 21.3 g of chlorine.

(M_r of Cl_2 = 71 and M_r of NaCl = 58.5)

$(1 \times 71) = 71$ g of Cl_2 makes $(2 \times 58.5) = 117$ g of NaCl

21.3 g of Cl_2 makes $117 \times \left(\dfrac{21.3}{71}\right)$ g of NaCl

= .... g   **(2 marks)**

3   Magnesium reacts with oxygen to form magnesium oxide:
$2Mg(s) + O_2(g) \rightarrow 2MgO(s)$

> Remember to calculate
> the relative formula mass,
> M_r, of oxygen gas and
> magnesium oxide first.

Calculate the maximum mass of magnesium oxide that
can be made from 12.6 g of oxygen.

(A_r of O = 16 and A_r of Mg = 24)

.... **(3 marks)**

4   Calcium carbonate decomposes, when heated, to form calcium oxide and carbon dioxide:

$CaCO_3(s) \rightarrow CaO(s) + CO_2(g)$

Calculate the maximum mass of calcium oxide that can be made from 12.5 kg of calcium carbonate.

(A_r of Ca = 40, A_r of C = 12 and A_r of O = 16)

.... **(3 marks)**

Had a go ☐ Nearly there ☐ Nailed it! ☐

Reacting mass calculations

1 Magnesium ribbon reacts with dilute hydrochloric acid. Magnesium chloride solution and hydrogen gas form: $Mg(s) + 2HCl(aq) \rightarrow MgCl_2(aq) + H_2(g)$

Which of the following statements about this reaction is correct?

> A **limiting reactant** is a reactant that is not in excess.

☐ **A** When magnesium is in excess, no magnesium is left when the reaction stops.

☐ **B** When hydrochloric acid is the limiting reactant, no liquid is left when the reaction stops.

☐ **C** When hydrochloric acid is in excess, some magnesium is left when the reaction stops.

☐ **D** When hydrochloric acid is the limiting reactant, some magnesium is left when the reaction stops.

(1 mark)

2 Copper carbonate decomposes when heated, forming copper oxide and carbon dioxide gas:

$$CuCO_3(s) \rightarrow CuO(s) + CO_2(g)$$

The graph shows how the mass of copper oxide formed depends on the mass of copper carbonate heated.

(a) Describe the relationship shown by the graph.

> **Maths skills** The mass of copper oxide formed is the **dependent variable** and the mass of copper carbonate heated is the **independent variable**. What happens to the dependent variable as the independent variable changes?

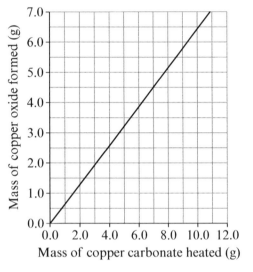

....

.... **(2 marks)**

(b) Explain why the mass of carbon dioxide formed depends on the mass of copper carbonate used.

....

.... **(2 marks)**

3 Iron is heated with excess chlorine gas, Cl_2, forming iron(III) chloride, $FeCl_3$.

Guided

11.2 g of iron produces 32.5 g of iron(III) chloride. Use this information to determine the stoichiometry of the reaction. (A_r of Fe = 56, M_r of Cl_2 = 71 and M_r of $FeCl_3$ = 162.5)

mass of chlorine reacted = 32.5 g – 11.2 g = ... g

amount of iron = $\dfrac{11.2}{56}$ = ... mol

amount of chlorine = $\dfrac{.............}{71}$ = ... mol

amount of iron(III) chloride = $\dfrac{32.5}{162.5}$ = ... mol

> Divide each number by the smallest number, then multiply all by the same whole number if necessary.

ratio of Fe : Cl_2 : $FeCl_3$ = ... : .... : ....

whole number ratio of Fe : Cl_2 : $FeCl_3$ = ... : .... : ....

so equation must be .... **(4 marks)**

Concentration of solution

1 Calculate the following volumes in dm^3.

| Maths skills | $1\ dm^3 = 1000\ cm^3$ |

(a) $2000\ cm^3$

.... **(1 mark)**

(b) $500\ cm^3$

.... **(1 mark)**

(c) $25\ cm^3$

.... **(1 mark)**

2 A student dissolves 10 g of copper sulfate in $250\ cm^3$ of water. Calculate the concentration of the solution formed in $g\ dm^{-3}$.

$concentration = \left(\dfrac{10}{250}\right) \times 1000 = $ .... **(1 mark)**

3 Calculate the concentrations of the following solutions in $g\ dm^{-3}$.

(a) 5.0 g of sodium hydroxide dissolved in $100\ cm^3$ of water

.... **(1 mark)**

(b) 14.6 g of hydrogen chloride dissolved in $400\ cm^3$ of water

.... **(1 mark)**

(c) 0.25 g of glucose dissolved in $25\ cm^3$ of water

.... **(1 mark)**

4 A school technician wants to make $2.5\ dm^3$ of a $40\ g\ dm^{-3}$ aqueous solution of sodium hydroxide.

(a) Describe the meaning of the term **aqueous solution**.

.... **(1 mark)**

(b) Calculate the mass of sodium hydroxide that the technician must dissolve to make her solution.

.... **(1 mark)**

(c) A student mixes $50\ cm^3$ of the technician's solution with $200\ cm^3$ of water.

Calculate the concentration of the student's sodium hydroxide solution in $g\ dm^{-3}$.

Mass of NaOH in $50\ cm^3 = 40 \times \dfrac{50}{1000} = $ .... g

New concentration $= \left(\dfrac{mass}{250}\right) \times 1000 = $ ....

.... **(2 marks)**

Guided

Guided

Avogadro's constant and moles

1 One mole, 1 mol, of particles of a substance contains 6.02×10^{23} particles.

State the name given to this number.

> **Maths skills** 6.02×10^{23} is a number expressed in standard form.
> You can enter it into your calculator as: 6.02 EXP 23.

.... **(1 mark)**

2 Calculate the mass of the following substances.

> The relative atomic mass, A_r, of carbon is 12. This means that 1 mol of carbon atoms has a mass of 12 g.

(a) 0.500 mol of xenon atoms, Xe (A_r of Xe = 131)

.... **(1 mark)**

(b) 1.5 mol of oxygen molecules, O_2 (A_r of O = 16)

.... **(1 mark)**

(c) 0.30 mol of ammonium ions, NH_4^+
(A_r of N = 14 and A_r of H = 1)

.... **(1 mark)**

3 Calculate the amount, in mol, of the following substances.

> **Guided**

(a) 6 g of carbon atoms, C (A_r of C = 12)

$amount = \dfrac{6}{12} = $ .... mol .... **(1 mark)**

(b) 45 g of water molecules, H_2O (A_r of H = 1 and A_r of O = 16)

.... **(1 mark)**

(c) 15 g of carbonate ions, CO_3^{2-} (A_r of C = 12 and A_r of O = 16)

.... **(1 mark)**

4 Calculate the amount of **atoms**, in mol, in the following substances.

(a) 1.0 mol of carbon dioxide molecules, CO_2

.... **(1 mark)**

(b) 0.5 mol of ethanoic acid molecules, CH_3COOH

.... **(1 mark)**

(c) 21.3 g of chlorine gas, Cl_2 (A_r of Cl = 35.5)

.... **(1 mark)**

5 Calculate the number of molecules in 2.25 mol of carbon dioxide molecules, CO_2.

.... **(1 mark)**

6 Calculate the amount of molecules, in mol, in 9.03×10^{24} molecules of water, H_2O.

.... **(1 mark)**

Extended response – Types of substance

Graphite and diamond are two different forms of carbon. The table shows some information about their properties. Copper, a soft metal used in electrical cables, is included for comparison.

Substance	Relative hardness	Relative electrical conductivity
graphite	10	10^8
copper	100	10^{10}
diamond	10 000	1

Higher values mean harder or better at conducting electricity.

Graphite is used to make electrodes and as a lubricant. Diamond is used in cutting tools. Explain each use in terms of the bonding and structure present. You should use information from the table in your answer.

You should be able to describe the structures of graphite and diamond.

It may help if you plan your answer before you start. For example, write separate answers about graphite and diamond. Include each given use and, using information from the table, the property important to that use. Make sure that you then explain how the substance's bonding and structure give it that property.

....

....

....

....

....

....

....

....

....

....

....

....

....

....

....

....

.... **(6 marks)**

Quick, labelled diagrams showing the structures of diamond and graphite may help your explanations.

States of matter

1 Iodine crystals become a purple vapour when they are warmed. What is the name for this state change?

> The crystals are in the solid state and the vapour is in the gas state.

☐ **A** melting   ☐ **C** subliming

☐ **B** boiling   ☐ **D** condensing   **(1 mark)**

2 Most substances can exist in the solid, liquid or gas states. Give the name of each state change below.

(a) liquid to solid

.... **(1 mark)**

(b) gas to liquid

.... **(1 mark)**

3 Water changes to steam when it is heated. State why this is a **physical** change.

.... **(1 mark)**

4 (a) Describe the arrangement, and movement, of particles in each state of matter.

> Is the arrangement regular or random? Are the particles close or far apart? How do the particles move?

solid ....

....

liquid ....

....

gas ....

.... **(6 marks)**

(b) Particles in all states have some stored energy.

Name the state in which the particles have the most stored energy, and justify your answer.

....

.... **(2 marks)**

5 Describe what happens to the arrangement, and movement, of particles when a substance changes from the liquid state to the solid state.

Guided

The arrangement changes from ....

and the movement changes from ....

.... **(2 marks)**

6 The melting point of substance **X** is −114°C and its boiling point is 78°C. Predict its state at −30°C.

.... **(1 mark)**

Pure substances and mixtures

1 (a) Explain why sodium, Na, and chlorine, Cl_2, are two different elements.

The atoms of an element all have the same ....

but atoms of Na and Cl_2 have different .... **(2 marks)**

(b) Explain why sodium chloride, NaCl, is defined as a compound.

....

.... **(2 marks)**

2 A student investigates three samples of water. She transfers 25 cm³ of each sample to weighed evaporating basins. She then heats the basins until all the water has evaporated, lets them cool and weighs them again.

The table shows the student's results.

Water sample	Mass of basin before adding water (g)	Mass of basin after evaporating water (g)	Difference in mass (g)
A	73.05	73.20	0.15
B	72.61	72.85	
C	74.40	74.43	

(a) Complete the table to show the difference in mass for water samples **B** and **C**.   **(1 mark)**

(b) Explain whether any of the water samples are pure.

....

.... **(2 marks)**

3 Solders are alloys used to join copper pipes or electrical components together. Some 'lead-free' solders are mixtures of tin and silver. The table shows the melting points of tin, silver and a lead-free solder.

Explain how the data show that the solder is a mixture.

> Look at how the melting points are shown for each substance.

Substance	Melting point (°C)
tin	232
silver	962
solder	220–229

....

....

.... **(2 marks)**

4 The boiling point of pure water is 100.0°C. A sample of seawater boils at 100.6°C.

(a) Seawater contains dissolved salts. State the effect of these salts on the boiling point of water.

.... **(1 mark)**

(b) A sample of seawater is boiled in an open container. Predict what will happen to the boiling point of the sample during this process, and justify your answer.

....

....

.... **(3 marks)**

Distillation

1 Which of the following is a suitable method to separate a mixture of two miscible liquids?

> Miscible liquids mix completely with each other.

  ☐ **A** filtration   ☐ **C** fractional distillation

  ☐ **B** simple distillation   ☐ **D** paper chromatography   **(1 mark)**

2 The apparatus shown in the diagram is used to separate the components of a seawater sample.

(a) Describe what happens to vapour from the seawater as it passes through the apparatus labelled **X**.

....

....

.... **(2 marks)**

> **Guided**

(b) Cold water passes through the condenser. Explain what happens to its temperature.

The temperature of the water .... because ....

.... **(2 marks)**

3 The apparatus shown in the diagram is used to separate a mixture of ethanol and water.

(a) Give a reason that explains why ethanol and water can be separated using the method shown.

.... **(1 mark)**

(b) Explain which liquid, ethanol or water, is collected first.

....

.... **(2 marks)**

(c) Give a reason that explains why the cold water supply should be connected at **Z** rather than **Y**.

....

.... **(1 mark)**

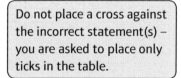

Filtration and crystallisation

1   A student filters a mixture of sand, salt and water. He collects the liquid that passes through the filter paper. Complete the table by placing a tick (✓) in the box against each correct statement.

Statement	Tick (✓)
The liquid is water.	
The liquid is the filtrate.	
The salt is left behind as a residue.	
The sand is left behind as a residue.	

Do not place a cross against the incorrect statement(s) – you are asked to place only ticks in the table.

(2 marks)

2   Potassium iodide solution reacts with lead nitrate solution. A mixture of potassium nitrate solution and insoluble yellow lead iodide forms. When this is filtered, lead iodide remains in the filter paper.

Guided

(a)   Balance the equation below, and give the state symbols for each substance.

......KI(aq) + Pb(NO$_3$)$_2$(......) → ......KNO$_3$(......) + PbI$_2$(......)   **(2 marks)**

(b)   The yellow lead iodide is washed, with distilled water, while it is on the filter paper.

(i)   State why the lead iodide does not pass through the filter paper.

.... **(1 mark)**

(ii)   Suggest a reason that explains why the lead iodide is washed.

.... **(1 mark)**

3   A student decides to make pure, dry copper chloride crystals. She adds an excess of insoluble copper carbonate to dilute hydrochloric acid. Copper chloride solution forms.

(a)   Name a suitable method to remove excess copper carbonate from the copper chloride solution.

.... **(1 mark)**

(b)   The student leaves her copper chloride solution on a windowsill.

(i)   Explain why crystals of copper chloride form after a few days.

....

....

.... **(3 marks)**

(ii)   Give a reason that explains why the student pours away the remaining solution, and then pats the crystals with filter paper.

.... **(1 mark)**

(c)   The student could heat her copper chloride solution instead of leaving it on a windowsill. Describe two steps that she should take to obtain large, regular-shaped crystals.

....

....

.... **(2 marks)**

Paper chromatography

1 Paper chromatography is used to determine whether an orange squash drink, **O**, contains an illegal food colouring, **X**.

Spots of each substance, and spots of three legal food colourings (**A**, **B** and **C**), are added to chromatography paper. The diagram shows the result of the chromatography experiment.

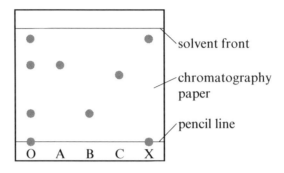

(a) Suggest a reason that explains why the start line is drawn using a pencil, rather than using ink.

.... **(1 mark)**

(b) Explain whether the orange squash, **O**, is a pure substance or a mixture.

....

.... **(2 marks)**

(c) Identify which legal food colourings (**A**, **B** or **C**) are present in the orange squash.

.... **(1 mark)**

(d) Explain whether the orange squash contains the illegal food colouring, **X**.

....

.... **(2 marks)**

(e) Suggest a reason that explains why one of the substances in **X** remains on the pencil line.

.... **(1 mark)**

2 The diagram shows a chromatogram of a dye.

Calculate the R_f value of the spot in the chromatogram.

$$R_f = \frac{\text{distance travelled by a spot}}{\text{distance travelled by the solvent front}}$$

35mm solvent front

28mm

start line

....

....

....

.... **(3 marks)**

🧪 Practical skills   **Investigating inks**

1 Paper chromatography is used to separate mixtures of coloured substances, such as those in inks.

(a) State two measurements that must be made so that an R_f value can be calculated.

....

.... **(2 marks)**

(b) Suggest reasons that explain why these measurements are recorded to the nearest millimetre, rather than to the nearest centimetre.

> 🖩 **Maths skills** You must be able to use appropriate apparatus to make and record a range of measurements accurately.

....

.... **(2 marks)**

2 Simple distillation is used to separate a solvent from a solution.

(a) Suggest reasons that explain why the solution must be heated **gently**.

....

.... **(2 marks)**

(b) During distillation, the solvent vapour may condense slowly without the use of a condenser. State one hazard caused by carrying out distillation without a condenser.

.... **(1 mark)**

3 A student investigates the composition of a sample of ballpoint pen ink. He uses propanone for the mobile phase in his paper chromatography. The diagram shows part of the label on a bottle of propanone.

> ⬥ ⬦
> Irritating to eyes.
> May cause skin dryness.
> Vapour causes dizziness.
> **Propanone CH_3COCH_3**

(a) State one hazard of propanone, shown by the label but not described in words.

.... **(1 mark)**

(b) Explain two precautions, other than eye protection, to control the risk of harm from propanone.

> You need to be able to use gases, liquids and solids safely and carefully.

....

....

.... **(2 marks)**

Drinking water

1 Waste water and ground water can be treated to make it safe to drink. Which word correctly describes water that is safe for us to drink?

☐ **A** potable

☐ **C** edible

☐ **B** fresh

☐ **D** filtered   **(1 mark)**

2 Chlorine is a toxic gas that dissolves in water.

(a) State why chlorine is used in water treatment.

> Your answer must be more precise than just 'to make it safe to drink'.

.... **(1 mark)**

(b) Suggest reasons that explain why drinking water that contains chlorine is considered safe to drink, even though chlorine gas is toxic.

....

.... **(2 marks)**

3 Name the two stages in water treatment that are carried out before chlorine is added. Give a reason why each stage is carried out.

> You do not have to place the two stages in a correct order in this question.

name of stage ....

reason ....

name of stage ....

reason .... **(4 marks)**

4 Explain why distilled water, rather than tap water, is used in chemical analysis.

⟩Guided⟩   Unlike tap water, distilled water does not contain ....

These would .... **(2 marks)**

5 Drinking water in the UK comes from fresh water including rivers, lakes and reservoirs. In some countries drinking water may come from seawater instead.

(a) Name the separation method used to separate water for drinking from seawater.

.... **(1 mark)**

(b) Suggest a reason that explains why producing drinking water from seawater is usually expensive.

.... **(1 mark)**

6 Aluminium sulfate may be added during water treatment. It forms a precipitate of aluminium hydroxide, which traps small particles suspended in the water. Balance the equation for this reaction.

$Al_2(SO_4)_3(aq) + ...H_2O(l) \rightarrow ......Al(OH)_3(s) + ...H_2SO_4(aq)$ **(1 mark)**

Extended response – Separating mixtures

A cloudy pale yellow mixture contains three substances (**A**, **B** and **C**).

The table shows some information about these substances.

Substance	Melting point (°C)	Boiling point (°C)	Notes
A	115	445	yellow, insoluble in **B** and **C**
B	−95	56	colourless, soluble in **C**
C	0	100	colourless, soluble in **B**

Devise a method to produce pure samples of each individual substance from the mixture.

> The command word **devise** means that you are being asked to plan or invent a procedure from existing principles or ideas. You do not have to imagine a complex method that goes beyond your GCSE studies.

You should use the information in the table in your answer, and explain why you have suggested each step.

> The separation methods covered at GCSE include simple distillation, fractional distillation, filtration, crystallisation and paper chromatography. You do not need to use them all to answer this question.

....

....

....

....

....

....

....

....

....

....

....

....

....

....

....

> You should be able to describe an appropriate experimental technique to separate a mixture if you know the properties of the components of the mixture.

.... **(6 marks)**

Acids and alkalis

1 A student adds a few drops of universal indicator solution to some dilute hydrochloric acid.

(a) The universal indicator solution is green before being added to the acid. State what this tells you about the pH of the universal indicator solution.

.... **(2 marks)**

(b) Give the colour of the mixture formed by the universal indicator solution and dilute hydrochloric acid.

.... **(1 mark)**

(c) Name the ion, produced by the hydrochloric acid, that is responsible for the colour change.

.... **(1 mark)**

2 A student heats some magnesium ribbon in air. It burns with a white flame and a white solid forms. The student then mixes the white solid with water in a test tube.

(a) Write a balanced equation for the reaction between magnesium and oxygen.

> You should be able to recall the formulae of elements and simple compounds.

.... **(2 marks)**

(b) Universal indicator solution turns purple when it is added to the mixture in the test tube. State what this tells you about the mixture.

.... **(1 mark)**

3 Sodium hydroxide dissolves in water to form an alkaline solution.

> **Guided**

Write a balanced equation, including state symbols, for the ionisation of sodium hydroxide in solution.

> Two different ions in aqueous solution form.

$NaOH(aq) \rightarrow Na$.. **(1 mark)**

4 Complete the table below to show the colours of litmus, methyl orange and phenolphthalein.

> **Guided**

Indicator	Colour at pH 14	Colour at pH 1
litmus	blue	red
methyl orange		
phenolphthalein		

> You should be able to recall the effect of acids and alkalis on these indicators.

(2 marks)

5 The pH of an acidic solution depends on the concentration of $H^+(aq)$ ions.

(a) State what happens to the pH of an acidic solution as the concentration of these ions is increased.

.... **(1 mark)**

(b) State what happens to the pH of an alkaline solution as the hydroxide ion concentration is increased.

.... **(1 mark)**

Strong and weak acids

1　A student adds water to a sample of an acid. The pH changes from 2 to 4. Which of the following statements about this change is correct?

> Answer **A** cannot be correct because the solution becomes less strongly acidic.

☐　**A**　The solution becomes more strongly acidic.

☐　**B**　The concentration of hydrogen ions increases 2 times.

☐　**C**　The concentration of hydrogen ions increases 100 times.

☐　**D**　The concentration of hydrogen ions decreases 100 times.　　**(1 mark)**

2　Nitric acid dissociates in aqueous solution: $HNO_3(aq) \rightarrow H^+(aq) + NO_3^-(aq)$

State why nitric acid is described as a **strong** acid.

Nitric acid is .... dissociated into ions in aqueous solution.　　**(1 mark)**

3　Methanoic acid dissociates in aqueous solution: $HCOOH(aq) \rightleftharpoons HCOO^-(aq) + H^+(aq)$

(a)　Give the meaning of the symbol $\rightleftharpoons$ in the equation.

....　**(1 mark)**

(b)　State why methanoic acid is described as a **weak** acid.

> The reason is **not** to do with the concentration of the methanoic acid.

....　**(1 mark)**

4　Explain, in terms of the amount of dissolved sodium hydroxide, the difference between concentrated sodium hydroxide solution and dilute sodium hydroxide solution.

....

....

....　**(2 marks)**

5　The table gives some information about two different acids.

(a)　Explain how the table shows that hydrochloric acid is a stronger acid than ethanoic acid.

Acid	pH of acid
0.2 mol dm^{-3} hydrochloric acid	0.70
0.02 mol dm^{-3} hydrochloric acid	1.70
0.2 mol dm^{-3} ethanoic acid	2.75

....

....　**(2 marks)**

(b)　Describe the effect of diluting hydrochloric acid on its pH.

....

....　**(2 marks)**

(c)　State why 0.0018 mol dm^{-3} of hydrochloric acid has the same pH as 0.2 mol dm^{-3} of ethanoic acid.

....　**(1 mark)**

Bases and alkalis

1 What forms when an acid reacts with a metal hydroxide?

☐ **A** a salt only ☐ **C** a salt and hydrogen only

☐ **B** a salt and water only ☐ **D** a salt and carbon dioxide only **(1 mark)**

2 Sodium carbonate, Na_2CO_3, reacts with dilute nitric acid:

sodium carbonate + nitric acid → sodium nitrate + carbon dioxide + water

Guided

(a) Write the balanced equation for this reaction.

.... + ... HNO_3 → + ... + ... + ... **(2 marks)**

(b) State two things that you would see when sodium carbonate powder is added to dilute nitric acid.

> You do not need to name any substances in your answer – make sure that you write down two observations.

....

.... **(2 marks)**

(c) Describe the chemical test for carbon dioxide.

> Write down what you would do and what you would expect to observe.

....

.... **(2 marks)**

3 Calcium reacts with dilute hydrochloric acid. Bubbles of gas are given off and a colourless solution forms. Some calcium remains in the bottom of the test tube when the reaction stops.

(a) Name the colourless solution that forms.

.... **(1 mark)**

(b) (i) Name the gas responsible for the bubbles.

.... **(1 mark)**

(ii) Describe the chemical test for the gas named in part **(i)**.

....

.... **(2 marks)**

4 Zinc oxide is an example of a base.

(a) Describe what is meant by a **base**.

....

.... **(2 marks)**

(b) State the general name for a **soluble** base.

.... **(1 mark)**

(c) Name the salt formed when zinc oxide reacts with dilute sulfuric acid.

.... **(1 mark)**

Practical skills

Neutralisation

1   An acid reacts with a base to form a salt and water only. Explain, in terms of reacting ions, what happens when an acid reacts with an alkali.

> Give the names or formulae of the reacting ions from the acid and alkali, and the product that they form.

....

....

.... **(3 marks)**

2   Write balanced equations for the reaction of dilute hydrochloric acid, HCl, with:

(a) calcium oxide powder, CaO

.... **(2 marks)**

(b) calcium hydroxide powder, $Ca(OH)_2$

.... **(2 marks)**

3   Suggest a reason that explains why a pH meter must be calibrated before it is used.

> You should be able to use appropriate apparatus and substances to measure pH in different situations.

.... **(1 mark)**

4   Limewater is calcium hydroxide solution. A student investigates what happens to the pH when he adds small portions of limewater to 25 cm^3 of dilute hydrochloric acid in a flask. The table shows his results.

Guided

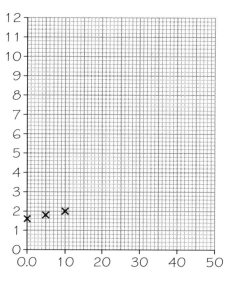

Volume of limewater added (cm^3)	pH of the mixture in the flask
0	1.6
5	1.8
10	2.0
15	2.2
20	2.6
24	3.8
25	7.0
26	10.4
30	11.2
35	11.5
40	11.6

Plot a graph to show these results.   **(3 marks)**

> **Maths skills** If you are asked to plot a graph, you need to mark the points accurately on the grid, then draw a line or curve of best fit. You must also work out a suitable scale and label the axes if this has not already been done for you.

🧪 Practical skills **Salts from insoluble bases**

1 Iron(II) oxide is an insoluble base. It reacts with dilute sulfuric acid to form iron(II) sulfate and water:

$$FeO(s) + H_2SO_4(aq) \rightarrow FeSO_4(aq) + H_2O(l)$$

This reaction can be used to prepare a solution that contains only the salt and water.

(a) Explain why an excess of iron(II) oxide is added to the dilute sulfuric acid.

> What substances are in the reaction mixture after adding the excess reactant?

....

.... **(2 marks)**

(b) Suggestion a reason that explains why the dilute sulfuric acid may be warmed before adding iron(II) oxide.

.... **(1 mark)**

(c) Name the separation method needed to remove the excess iron(II) oxide.

.... **(1 mark)**

(d) Name the process used to produce iron(II) sulfate crystals from the iron(II) sulfate solution.

.... **(1 mark)**

2 A student wants to prepare pure, dry crystals of copper sulfate. This is her method.

Making copper sulfate crystals

A Put 25 cm³ of dilute sulfuric acid in a beaker.
B Add several spatulas of copper oxide powder together.
C Pour the liquid from the beaker into an evaporating basin.
D Heat the liquid using a blue Bunsen burner flame until all the water has boiled away.

(a) Name a suitable piece of apparatus to measure 25 cm³ of dilute sulfuric acid at step A.

.... **(1 mark)**

(b) Describe **two** improvements the student could make at step B, and give reasons for your answers.

improvement 1 ....

....

improvement 2 ....

.... **(4 marks)**

(c) The method used at step D produces poorly formed, small crystals. Describe how the student should modify the method and apparatus used at step D to produce larger, well-formed crystals safely.

....

....

> You should be able to use appropriate heating methods including use of a Bunsen burner and a water bath.

.... **(2 marks)**

Practical skills

Salts from soluble bases

1 Which of the following is a suitable method to prepare a soluble salt from an acid and an alkali?

☐ **A** precipitation

☐ **B** filtration

☐ **C** titration

☐ **D** distillation **(1 mark)**

nitric acid

sodium hydroxide + indicator

2 The diagram shows the apparatus used to add known volumes of dilute nitric acid to a measured volume of sodium hydroxide solution.

Complete the diagram to show the names of the pieces of apparatus shown. **(2 marks)**

3 A student prepares sodium chloride solution using the apparatus shown in question **2**.

(a) Name the acid that the student should use in his experiment.

.... **(1 mark)**

(b) Name a piece of apparatus, more accurate than a measuring cylinder, that the student could use to measure 25.0 cm^3 of sodium hydroxide solution.

.... **(1 mark)**

(c) The student uses phenolphthalein indicator. Describe the expected colour change at the end-point.

> You need to give the colour at the start and at the end.

.... **(1 mark)**

Guided (d) The student carries out a rough run, then three accurate runs. The table shows his results.

Run number	Rough	1	2	3
End reading (cm^3)	26.20	24.90	49.30	24.70
Start reading (cm^3)	0.10	0.00	24.90	0.20
Titre (cm^3)	26.10			

(i) Suggest a reason that explains why the student carries out a rough run first.

.... **(1 mark)**

(ii) Complete the table to show the titres for all four runs. **(1 mark)**

(iii) Calculate the mean titre from the accurate runs, ignoring any anomalous (outlier) titre.

.... cm^3 **(2 marks)**

(e) Describe how the student should use his mean titre when preparing pure sodium chloride solution.

....

....

.... **(2 marks)**

Making insoluble salts

1 Potassium chloride is a metal chloride that is soluble in water. Which of the following metal chlorides is insoluble in water?

> You need to be able to recall the general rules for the solubility of common types of substances in water.

☐ **A** sodium chloride

☐ **B** silver chloride

☐ **C** copper chloride

☐ **D** zinc chloride   **(1 mark)**

2 Which of the following pairs contains one substance that is soluble in water and one that is insoluble in water?

☐ **A** lead chloride and barium sulfate

☐ **B** calcium nitrate and potassium hydroxide

☐ **C** aluminium hydroxide and copper carbonate

☐ **D** ammonium carbonate and calcium sulfate   **(1 mark)**

3 A student wants to produce insoluble calcium hydroxide.

(a) Name two solutions that, when mixed together, will produce a precipitate of calcium hydroxide.

solution 1 ....

solution 2 .... **(2 marks)**

(b) Name the other product formed when the two solutions named in part (**a**) are mixed together.

.... **(1 mark)**

4 Sodium carbonate, Na_2CO_3, and calcium chloride, $CaCl_2$, are soluble in water. Calcium carbonate, $CaCO_3$, is insoluble in water.

(a) Write a balanced equation for the reaction between sodium carbonate solution and calcium chloride solution. Include state symbols in your answer.

> There are two products of this reaction, including calcium carbonate.

.... **(2 marks)**

(b) Describe how you would use solid sodium carbonate and solid calcium chloride to produce a pure, dry sample of calcium carbonate.

> Remember that you are starting with solid reactants.

....

....

....

....

.... **(4 marks)**

5 Explain why a precipitate forms when dilute sulfuric acid and lead nitrate solution are mixed together.

> Guided

Sulfuric acid contains .... ions which react with .... ions

to form .... **(3 marks)**

Extended response – Making salts

Sodium chloride solution can be made from dilute hydrochloric acid and sodium hydroxide solution:

$$HCl(aq) + NaOH(aq) \rightarrow NaCl(aq) + H_2O(l)$$

Devise a titration experiment to find the exact volume of hydrochloric acid needed to neutralise 25.0 cm^3 of sodium hydroxide solution. Explain how you would use the result from this experiment to obtain pure, dry, sodium chloride crystals.

> It may help to plan your answers to questions similar to this one. For example, you could divide your answer here into three sections:
> * setting up the apparatus ready for a titration, including where the reagents need to go
> * carrying out the titration, including steps needed to obtain an accurate result
> * producing sodium chloride crystals from sodium chloride solution.

....

....

....

....

....

....

....

....

....

....

....

....

....

....

....

....

....

....

> You should be able to describe how to carry out an acid–alkali titration using a burette, a pipette and a suitable indicator, to prepare a pure, dry salt.

....

....

....

.... **(6 marks)**

Electrolysis

1 Under what conditions can an ionic compound conduct electricity?

> Molten substances are in the liquid state.

☐ **A** only when it is molten

☐ **B** when it is solid or molten

☐ **C** when it is solid or in solution

☐ **D** when it is molten or in solution

(1 mark)

2 State what is meant by the term **electrolyte**.

> **Guided**

An electrolyte is an .... compound in the .... state

or .... **(2 marks)**

3 A student places a purple crystal of potassium manganate(VII), $KMnO_4$, on a damp piece of filter paper. She connects each end of the paper to a d.c. electricity supply. A purple streak gradually moves to the left.

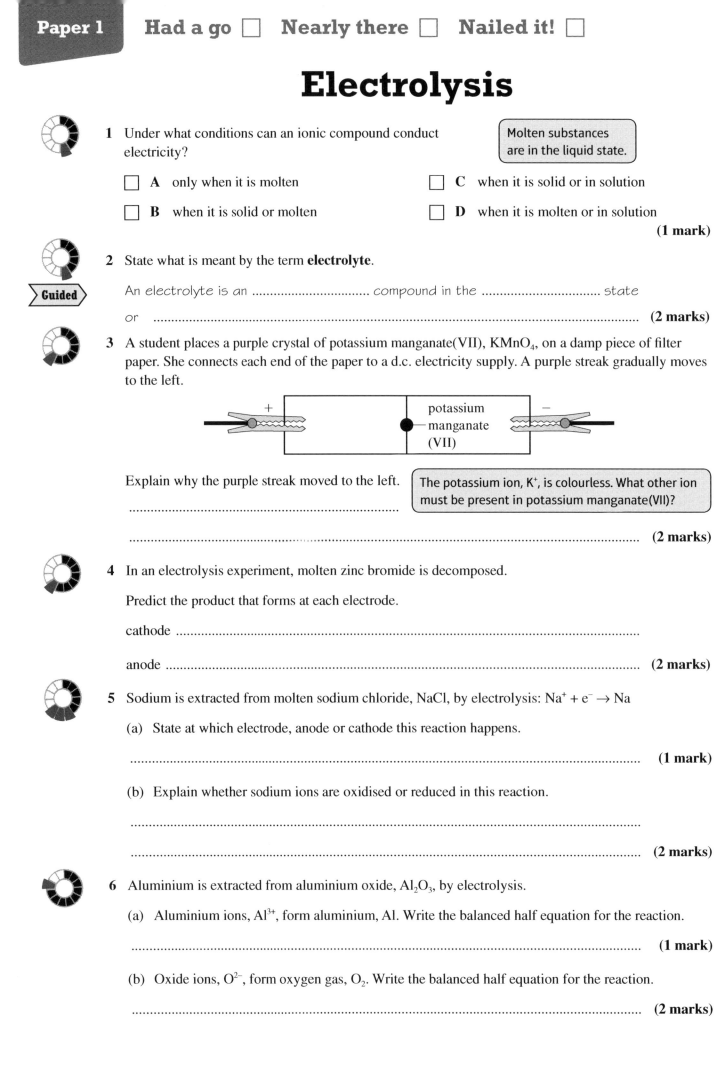

Explain why the purple streak moved to the left.

> The potassium ion, K^+, is colourless. What other ion must be present in potassium manganate(VII)?

....

.... **(2 marks)**

4 In an electrolysis experiment, molten zinc bromide is decomposed.

Predict the product that forms at each electrode.

cathode ....

anode .... **(2 marks)**

5 Sodium is extracted from molten sodium chloride, NaCl, by electrolysis: $Na^+ + e^- \rightarrow Na$

(a) State at which electrode, anode or cathode this reaction happens.

.... **(1 mark)**

(b) Explain whether sodium ions are oxidised or reduced in this reaction.

....

.... **(2 marks)**

6 Aluminium is extracted from aluminium oxide, Al_2O_3, by electrolysis.

(a) Aluminium ions, Al^{3+}, form aluminium, Al. Write the balanced half equation for the reaction.

.... **(1 mark)**

(b) Oxide ions, O^{2-}, form oxygen gas, O_2. Write the balanced half equation for the reaction.

.... **(2 marks)**

Electrolysing solutions

1 The ions in copper chloride solution are:

- copper ions, Cu^{2+}
- chloride ions, Cl^-
- hydrogen ions, H^+
- hydroxide ions, OH^-

Copper chloride solution is electrolysed using a d.c. electricity supply.

(a) Which of these ions will be attracted to the cathode during the electrolysis of copper chloride solution?

☐ **A** Cl^- ions only

☐ **C** H^+ ions only

☐ **B** Cl^- ions and OH^- ions

☐ **D** H^+ and Cu^{2+} ions   **(1 mark)**

Guided

(b) Explain, with the help of an equation, why the copper chloride solution contains H^+ ions and OH^- ions.

Some water molecules ....

.... **(2 marks)**

(c) Chloride ions, Cl^-, form chlorine gas, Cl_2. Write the balanced half equation for the reaction.

.... **(2 marks)**

2 The electrolysis of concentrated sodium chloride solution, $NaCl(aq)$, produces two useful gases.

(a) Write the formulae of all the ions present in a concentrated sodium chloride solution.

.... **(2 marks)**

(b) Predict the gas that forms at:

(i) the anode .... **(1 mark)**

(ii) the cathode .... **(1 mark)**

(c) Explain why the solution remaining after electrolysis is alkaline.

....

.... **(2 marks)**

3 Oxygen is produced at the anode during the electrolysis of sodium sulfate solution.

Explain how the oxygen is formed from ions in the solution.

> Which negatively charged ions will be present in this solution? Which of these will be discharged at the anode? You could answer in words or using a balanced half equation.

....

.... **(2 marks)**

4 Hydrogen and oxygen are produced during the electrolysis of water. Suggest a reason that explains why electrolysis happens faster when the water is acidified with dilute sulfuric acid.

....

.... **(2 marks)**

Practical skills # Investigating electrolysis

1 The products formed from copper sulfate solution, $CuSO_4(aq)$, depend on the type of electrode used:

- Graphite electrodes are inert electrodes – they just provide a surface for electrode reactions to happen.

- Copper electrodes are non-inert electrodes – they take part in electrode reactions with copper ions.

(a) Oxygen forms during the electrolysis of copper sulfate solution using graphite electrodes.

Explain at which electrode (anode or cathode) oxygen will be produced.

....

.... **(2 marks)**

(b) The anode loses copper during the electrolysis of copper sulfate solution with copper electrodes.

Write the balanced half equation for the formation of copper ions, Cu^{2+}, from copper.

.... **(2 marks)**

2 The electrolysis of copper sulfate solution, using copper electrodes, is used to purify copper. During electrolysis, the copper anode loses mass. The copper cathode gains mass because copper is deposited.

(a) Write the balanced half equation for the formation of copper from copper ions, Cu^{2+}.

.... **(2 marks)**

(b) A student investigates the gain in mass by a copper cathode. She runs each experiment for the same time, but changes the current. She measures the mass of the cathode before and after electrolysis. The graph shows her results.

(i) Identify the variable controlled by the student in her experiment.

....

....**(1 mark)**

(ii) Identify the dependent variable in the student's experiment.

....

....**(1 mark)**

(iii) Calculate the gradient of the line of best fit. Give your answer to two significant figures.

A linear relationship such as this can be represented by: $y = mx + c$ (m is the gradient and c is the intercept on the vertical axis (y-axis). The gradient equals the change on the y-axis, divided by the change on the x-axis.

.... g/A **(3 marks)**

Extended response – Electrolysis

A student carries out two experiments using copper chloride, $CuCl_2$.

In experiment 1, the student places two graphite electrodes into copper chloride powder in a beaker. She then connects the electrodes to a d.c. electricity supply and records any changes.

For experiment 2, the student disconnects the d.c. supply, then adds some water to dissolve the copper chloride. She reconnects the electrodes to the d.c. supply and records any changes.

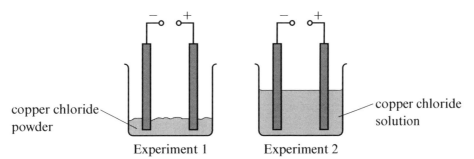

copper chloride powder

copper chloride solution

Experiment 1   Experiment 2

The table shows the student's results.

Experiment	Observations at the cathode (–)	Observations at the anode (+)
1	no visible change	no visible change
2	brown solid forms on the electrode	bubbles of a yellow-green gas released

Explain the differences between the results shown in the table for experiments 1 and 2.

> Explain why copper chloride powder does not conduct electricity, and then explain why copper chloride solution does conduct electricity. Name the substances responsible for the student's observations.

....

....

....

....

....

....

....

....

....

....

....

....

.... **(6 marks)**

> You should explain, in terms of ions, why each substance forms. You could include half equations for this.

The reactivity series

1 Four metals (**W**, **X**, **Y** and **Z**) are added to cold water and to dilute hydrochloric acid. The table shows what happens.

Metal	Observations in water	Observations in dilute hydrochloric acid
W	slow bubbling	very fast bubbling
X	no visible change	no visible change
Y	fast bubbling	very fast bubbling
Z	no visible change	slow bubbling

(a) Which of the following shows the order of reactivity, from most reactive to least reactive metal?

☐ **A** W, Y, X, Z   ☐ **C** Y, W, X, Z

☐ **B** X, Z, W, Y   ☐ **D** Y, W, Z, X   **(1 mark)**

(b) The concentration of hydrochloric acid is kept the same each time. Give two other variables that should be kept the same in each experiment so that the reactivity of the metals can be compared.

....

.... **(2 marks)**

2 Magnesium reacts slowly with cold water to produce magnesium hydroxide, $Mg(OH)_2$.

> This flammable gas is produced when any metal reacts with water or with dilute acids.

(a) Name the gas produced in the reaction.

.... **(1 mark)**

(b) Write the balanced equation for the reaction between magnesium and water.

.... **(2 marks)**

(c) Name the compound formed when magnesium reacts with steam, rather than with cold water.

.... **(1 mark)**

3 Aluminium is protected from contact with water by a natural layer of aluminium oxide, Al_2O_3. This means that aluminium does not react with water, even though it is a reactive metal. However, aluminium does react with dilute acids, such as dilute sulfuric acid.

> Guided

(a) Write the balanced equation for the reaction between aluminium oxide and dilute sulfuric acid.

$Al_2O_3 + $ ....$H_2SO_4 \rightarrow Al_2(SO_4)_3 + $ ....H_2O **(1 mark)**

(b) Aluminium reacts with dilute sulfuric acid to form aluminium sulfate solution and a flammable gas.

Write the balanced equation for this reaction. Include state symbols in your answer.

.... **(3 marks)**

(c) There is no immediate visible change when aluminium is added to dilute sulfuric acid. Bubbling then starts and gets increasingly faster. Suggest reasons that explain these observations.

....

....

.... **(2 marks)**

Metal displacement reactions

1 Copper can displace silver from silver nitrate solution. Copper nitrate solution also forms in the reaction.

(a) Give a reason that explains why copper can displace silver from silver salts in solution.

> Which metal, copper or silver, is the more reactive of the two metals?

.... **(1 mark)**

(b) Write the balanced equation for the reaction between copper and silver nitrate solution. Include state symbols in your answer.

...........(.......) + ...$AgNO_3$(.......) → ....(......) + $Cu(NO_3)_2$(.......)   **(3 marks)**

2 A student investigates the reactivities of four metals, copper, magnesium, zinc and X. She adds pieces of magnesium ribbon to solutions of the nitrates of each metal. She then removes and examines each piece of magnesium ribbon after a few minutes. The table shows her results.

Solution	Observations
copper nitrate	brown coating on the magnesium ribbon
magnesium nitrate	no visible change
zinc nitrate	no visible change
X nitrate	grey coating on the magnesium ribbon

(a) Name the substance found in the brown coating on the magnesium ribbon.

.... **(1 mark)**

(b) Give a reason that explains why there is no visible change when magnesium nitrate solution is used.

.... **(1 mark)**

(c) The student repeats the experiment but she uses pieces of metal X instead of magnesium ribbon. The table shows her results.

Solution	Observations
copper nitrate	brown coating on the piece of metal X
magnesium nitrate	no visible change
zinc nitrate	grey coating on the piece of metal X
X nitrate	no visible change

Use the results shown in both tables to place the four metals in order of **decreasing** reactivity.

most reactive ....

....

....

least reactive .... **(2 marks)**

3 The thermite reaction makes molten iron for welding railway lines:

$2Al(s) + Fe_2O_3(s) \rightarrow Al_2O_3(s) + 2Fe(l)$

Explain what this reaction shows about the relative reactivity of aluminium and iron.

....

.... **(2 marks)**

Explaining metal reactivity

1 Give the meaning of the term **cation**.

A cation is a .... charged ion.   **(1 mark)**

2 Calcium is a reactive metal. It reacts vigorously with dilute hydrochloric acid to form calcium chloride solution and hydrogen gas: $Ca(s) + 2HCl(aq) \rightarrow CaCl_2(aq) + H_2(g)$

(a) The formula for a chloride ion is Cl^-. Deduce the formula for a calcium ion.

.... **(1 mark)**

(b) Describe what happens when a calcium atom becomes a calcium ion.

> The outer shell is involved when atoms of an element take part in reactions.

....

.... **(2 marks)**

(c) The table shows a reactivity series for the metals. Hydrogen is a non-metal. It is included for comparison.

> The more easily a metal's atoms form cations, the more reactive the metal is.

Identify the metal that:

(i) forms cations most easily

.... **(1 mark)**

(ii) forms cations least easily.

.... **(1 mark)**

potassium	most reactive
sodium	
calcium	
magnesium	
aluminium	
zinc	
iron	
(hydrogen)	
copper	
silver	
gold	least reactive

(d) Identify a metal that will **not** react with dilute acids.

.... **(1 mark)**

3 Metal displacement reactions are **redox** reactions.

(a) Zinc displaces copper from copper sulfate solution: $Zn(s) + CuSO_4(aq) \rightarrow ZnSO_4(aq) + Cu(s)$

Explain this reaction in terms of the tendency to form cations.

....

.... **(2 marks)**

(b) Write balanced half equations for:

(i) the oxidation of magnesium to form magnesium ions in aqueous solution

$Mg(s) \rightarrow$ .... **(2 marks)**

(ii) the reduction of hydrogen ions in an acidic solution to form hydrogen gas.

........$H^+(aq) +$ .... $\rightarrow$ .... **(2 marks)**

Metal ores

1 Tungsten metal is extracted from tungsten oxide. The tungsten oxide is heated in a stream of hydrogen gas:

$$WO_3 + 3H_2 \rightarrow W + 3H_2O$$

(a) What happens in this reaction?

☐ **A** Tungsten is oxidised.   ☐ **C** Hydrogen is reduced.

☐ **B** Tungsten oxide is reduced.   ☐ **D** Water is oxidised.   **(1 mark)**

(b) Suggest a reason that explains why this process is hazardous.

> Look at the reactants and products – are any of them hazardous?

.... **(1 mark)**

2 Metals are extracted from their ores. Give the meaning of the term **ore**.

A rock or mineral that contains ....

.... **(2 marks)**

3 Explain why some metals are found in the Earth's crust as uncombined elements.

....

.... **(2 marks)**

4 Cassiterite is a tin ore that contains tin oxide, SnO_2. Tin is extracted from tin oxide by heating with powdered carbon. Carbon monoxide, CO, also forms in the reaction.

(a) Write a balanced equation for the reaction.

.... **(2 marks)**

(b) Explain, in terms of gain or loss of oxygen, whether tin oxide is oxidised or reduced.

....

.... **(2 marks)**

5 Corrosion occurs when a metal oxidises, and this process continues. For example, sodium is shiny when it is freshly cut, but a dull layer of sodium oxide, Na_2O, forms quickly when sodium is exposed to air.

(a) Write a balanced equation for the reaction between sodium and oxygen gas, forming sodium oxide.

.... **(2 marks)**

(b) Suggest a reason that explains why copper oxidises slowly unless it is heated strongly.

.... **(1 mark)**

6 One of the stages in the extraction of titanium metal involves heating titanium chloride with sodium:

$$TiCl_4 + 4Na \rightarrow Ti + 4NaCl$$

(a) The formula for a chloride ion is Cl^-. Deduce the formula for a titanium ion.

.... **(1 mark)**

(b) Explain, in terms of gain or loss of electrons, whether titanium ions are oxidised or reduced.

....

.... **(2 marks)**   **49**

Iron and aluminium

1 The table shows a reactivity series for the metals.

Carbon is a non-metal. It is included for comparison.

Name a metal in the table that:

sodium	most reactive
calcium	
magnesium	
(carbon)	↓
zinc	
copper	least reactive

(a) is likely to be extracted from its ore using electrolysis.

.... **(1 mark)**

(b) could be extracted from its ore by heating with carbon.

.... **(1 mark)**

2 Haematite is an iron ore. It contains iron(III) oxide, Fe_2O_3.

Describe how iron is extracted from this ore. In your answer, include a balanced equation for the reaction.

> Iron is placed between zinc and copper in the reactivity series.

....

.... **(3 marks)**

3 Bauxite is an aluminium ore. It contains aluminium oxide, Al_2O_3.

Aluminium is extracted from purified aluminium oxide by electrolysis.

⟩**Guided**⟩   (a) Explain why aluminium oxide must be molten or dissolved for electrolysis to occur.

The ions in the electrolyte must be ....

.... **(2 marks)**

(b) Aluminium oxide is dissolved in molten cryolite, rather than being heated to melt it.

Suggest a reason that explains why this is done.

> Think about the amounts of energy involved in each case.

.... **(1 mark)**

(c) Write half equations for the reactions that happen at each electrode during the electrolysis of aluminium oxide.

at the anode ....

at the cathode .... **(4 marks)**

4 Aluminium is more abundant than iron in the Earth's crust. On average, the crust contains 8.2% aluminium but only 6.3% iron, although aluminium costs about six times more than iron.

> What is likely to be the main reason why extracting aluminium is more expensive than extracting iron?

Suggest reasons that explain the difference in the cost of the two metals.

....

.... **(2 marks)**

Biological metal extraction

1 Most **high-grade** copper ores have been used up. This means that copper must be extracted from **low-grade** ores. These have only low concentrations of copper compounds.

Phytoextraction is one way to extract copper from low-grade ores.

(a) The table shows the main steps involved in phytoextraction. Give the correct order by writing the numbers 1 to 5 in the correct boxes, where step 1 is the first step.

Step number	Process
	Copper ions become concentrated in compounds in plants.
	Copper is extracted from ash with a high concentration of copper compounds.
	Plants absorb copper ions through their roots.
1	Sow plants on ground containing low-grade copper ore.
	Plants are harvested and burned.

(1 mark)

(b) Energy is transferred to the environment, mainly by heating, when plants are burned. Suggest reasons that explain why this may be useful to a company extracting copper by phytoextraction.

....

.... (2 marks)

(c) Describe a disadvantage of extracting copper by phytoextraction.

....

.... (1 mark)

2 Bioleaching is one way to extract copper from low-grade ores. Reactions involving bacteria cause the slow conversion of copper sulfide to a mixture of copper sulfate solution and sulfuric acid.

(a) Suggest a reason that explains why the formation of sulfuric acid may be harmful to the environment.

.... (1 mark)

(b) The copper sulfate solution is very dilute. Scrap iron is used to produce copper from this solution.

(i) Write a balanced equation for the reaction between iron and copper sulfate solution, forming iron(II) sulfate solution and copper. Include state symbols in your answer.

> Copper ions have the formula Cu^{2+}, iron(II) ions have the formula Fe^{2+} and sulfate ions are SO_4^{2-}.

.... (3 marks)

(ii) State why iron is able to displace copper in this reaction.

.... (1 mark)

(iii) Give an advantage of using scrap iron to produce copper.

> Which metal is more valuable, copper or iron?

....

.... (1 mark)

Recycling metals

1 Some metals are found uncombined in the Earth's crust, but most metals are found as compounds in rocks.

(a) What name is given to any rocks from which metals can be extracted?

> Answer D cannot be correct because quarries are places where these rocks are removed from the ground.

☐ **A** oxides

☐ **C** limestone

☐ **B** ores

☐ **D** quarries   **(1 mark)**

(b) Describe two ways in which large-scale removal of rocks from the ground damages the environment.

....

.... **(2 marks)**

2 Around 90% of the lead produced each year is used in traditional 'lead acid' batteries for cars and other vehicles. About 70% of the lead used each year is recycled lead.

Guided

(a) Describe an advantage of recycling lead from lead acid batteries, rather than recycling lead from general scrap metal waste.

> Think about how different metals are obtained from scrap metal waste.

Most lead for recycling is found in ....

so lead does not need to be .... **(2 marks)**

(b) Describe two advantages of recycling metals, rather than extracting them from their compounds.

....

.... **(2 marks)**

3 Food cans are made from either steel coated with tin or aluminium. The table shows some information about these three metals.

Metal	Abundance in the Earth's crust (%)	Cost of 1 tonne of metal (£)	Energy saved by recycling (%)
steel	6.3	500	70
tin	0.000 22	16 500	75
aluminium	8.2	1500	94

(a) Some people believe that it may be more important to recycle tin, rather than steel or aluminium. Justify this statement using information from the table.

> **Maths skills** Use evidence from the table to support this statement.

....

.... **(2 marks)**

(b) The mass of metal used each year should also be taken into account when assessing the advantages of recycling a particular metal. Suggest a reason that explains why this is so.

....

.... **(1 mark)**

Life-cycle assessments

1 A life-time assessment for a manufactured product involves considering its effect on the environment at all stages.

Guided

The table shows the main steps involved in a life-time assessment. Give the correct order by writing the numbers 1 to 4 in the correct boxes, where step 1 is the first.

Step number	Process
	manufacturing the product
	obtaining raw materials
4	disposing of the product
	using the product

(1 mark)

2 Manufacturers can make glass bottles with thinner walls than in the past. A bottle for a fizzy drink had a mass of 240 g in 1996 but a mass of 190 g in 2016.

(a) 16.5 MJ/kg of glass is used in their manufacture.

Calculate the energy, in MJ, needed to make one bottle in 1996.

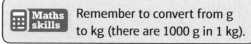

Maths skills Remember to convert from g to kg (there are 1000 g in 1 kg).

.... MJ **(2 marks)**

(b) Carbon dioxide, CO_2, is a greenhouse gas. The manufacture of glass bottles causes the emission of 1.2 kg CO_2/kg glass. Calculate the difference, between 1996 and 2016, in the mass of carbon dioxide emitted when one bottle is made.

....

.... **(2 marks)**

3 Window frames may be made from either PVC (a polymer) or wood. The table shows some information from a life-cycle assessment of a window frame.

Process	Energy used (MJ)	
	PVC frame	**Wooden frame**
producing the material	12.0	4.0
making the frame	3.0	3.6
transport and installation	4.2	4.8
maintenance	0.3	1.5
disposal in landfill	0.7	0.8

(a) Identify the stage in the life cycle of **each** window frame that is responsible for the most energy use.

.... **(1 mark)**

(b) Explain which type of frame is likely to have the lower environmental impact **when in use**.

....

.... **(2 marks)**

(c) The disposal of a PVC frame uses less energy than the disposal of a wooden frame. Suggest a reason that explains why this should not be the only measure of the environmental impact of disposal.

What happens to the frames after they have been buried in a landfill site?

.... **(1 mark)**

Extended response – Reactivity of metals

Magnesium forms cations more readily than copper. A spatula of magnesium powder mixed with a spatula of copper oxide powder is heated strongly on a steel lid. Magnesium oxide and copper are produced:

magnesium + copper oxide → magnesium oxide + copper

$$Mg(s) + CuO(s) \rightarrow MgO(s) + Cu(s)$$

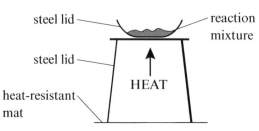

The reaction shows that magnesium is more reactive than copper. It is a very vigorous reaction. Energy is transferred to the surroundings by light and heating, and hot powder escapes into the air.

Devise an experiment, based on this method, to investigate the relative reactivity of copper, iron and zinc. In your answer, describe the results you expect, and explain how you would use them to deduce the order of reactivity. Explain how you would control the risks of harm in the investigation.

> Think about how many combinations of a metal powder and a metal oxide powder you will need to test.

> One way to show these combinations, and the expected results, is to make a completed results table.

....

....

....

....

....

....

....

....

....

....

....

....

> You should be able to evaluate the risks in a practical procedure, and suggest suitable precautions for a range of practicals (not just those mentioned in the specification).

....

....

.... **(6 marks)**

Transition metals

1 Iron is a transition metal. Which of these is a property of pure iron?

   ☐ **A** It has a low melting point.   ☐ **C** It has a high density.

   ☐ **B** It is a poor conductor of electricity.   ☐ **D** It is brittle.   **(1 mark)**

2 Describe where the transition metals are found in the periodic table.

Guided

Between groups ....

in the .... part of the periodic table............................ **(2 marks)**

3 Iron forms coloured compounds. For example, iron(II) hydroxide, Fe(OH)$_2$, is green. Iron(III) hydroxide, Fe(OH)$_3$ is orange–brown.

  (a) Explain what the Roman numbers in brackets, (II) and (III), mean.

                | The formula for the hydroxide ion is OH$^-$. What are the formulae of the iron ions in the two compounds? |

   ....

   .... **(2 marks)**

  (b) Magnesium hydroxide, Mg(OH)$_2$, and aluminium hydroxide, Al(OH)$_3$, are white. Explain why magnesium and aluminium form white compounds, but iron forms coloured compounds.

                | Where are these elements located in the periodic table? |

   ....

   .... **(2 marks)**

4 The Haber process is an industrial process for the manufacture of ammonia, NH$_3$. It requires nitrogen, hydrogen and iron. The balanced equation that models the process is: N$_2$(g) + 3H$_2$(g) → 2NH$_3$(g)

Describe the role of iron in the Haber process. Use the equation to justify your answer.

....

....

....

.... **(3 marks)**

5 The table shows the melting points of five metal elements (**A**, **B**, **C**, **D** and **E**).

Metal	A	B	C	D	E
Melting point (°C)	98	1244	−39	328	232

  (a) Identify the metal that could be mercury.

   .... **(1 mark)**

  (b) Identify a metal, other than your answer to part (**a**), that is likely to be a transition metal.

   .... **(1 mark)**

Rusting

1 (a) Name the two substances needed for iron to rust.

.... **(1 mark)**

(b) Name the iron compound that forms when iron rusts.

.... **(1 mark)**

2 The rusting of iron and steel objects can be prevented in different ways.

> **Guided**

(a) Explain how oiling stops a steel bicycle chain rusting.

The layer of oil stops ....

.... **(2 marks)**

(b) Steel screws for use on boats may be electroplated with nickel.

Give two reasons why metal objects may be electroplated.

....

.... **(2 marks)**

3 Titanium and iron are both transition metals. Titanium is more reactive than iron but it does not corrode in air. An invisible layer of titanium oxide forms naturally on the surface of titanium when exposed to the air.

> Unlike rust, this layer does not flake off the surface of the metal.

Describe how this layer prevents titanium from corroding.

.... **(1 mark)**

4 Car body panels made from steel are usually coated with zinc before they are painted. The zinc acts as another barrier in case the paint is damaged. It continues to prevent rusting, even if the zinc layer is also damaged.

(a) Give the name of the process by which iron or steel is coated with a layer of **zinc**.

.... **(1 mark)**

(b) (i) Give the name of the type of rust prevention shown by a damaged layer of zinc.

.... **(1 mark)**

(ii) Explain how this type of rust prevention works.

....

.... **(2 marks)**

5 Food cans are made from steel coated with a thin layer of tin. Unlike coating with zinc, a layer of tin does not continue to protect the steel below if it is damaged. Instead, the tin is oxidised to tin oxide, SnO_2.

Write a half equation for the oxidation of tin atoms to tin ions, Sn^{4+}.

.... **(2 marks)**

Alloys

1 Brass is made by dissolving hot pieces of zinc in molten copper, and then letting the mixture cool and solidify. What type of substance is brass?

☐ **A** a compound   ☐ **C** an alloy

☐ **B** an element   ☐ **D** an ore   **(1 mark)**

2 The diagrams show the structures of pure aluminium, and an alloy of aluminium and magnesium.

pure aluminium   alloy

(a) Give the name of this alloy.

.... **(1 mark)**

(b) Explain, in terms of their structures, why the alloy is stronger than pure aluminium.

....

....

.... **(3 marks)**

3 Explain why gold is used to make jewellery.

> Think about the physical and chemical properties of gold that make it suitable for use as a metal for jewellery.

....

.... **(2 marks)**

4 Iron is alloyed with other metals to produce alloy steels. These metals are more useful than pure iron. For example, they may be stronger. Apart from increasing their strength, describe one way in which alloy steels are more useful than pure iron.

> Think about some properties and uses of alloy steels compared with pure iron.

Guided

Pure iron rusts but stainless steel ....

.... **(2 marks)**

5 The table shows some information about aluminium and copper.

Metal	Relative strength	Relative electrical conductivity	Corrosion resistance	Density (g/cm³)
aluminium	2.2	0.6	good	2.70
copper	1.0	1.0	good	8.92

Assess which metal, aluminium or copper, is most suitable for overhead electricity cables.

> Identify the most relevant factors and come to a conclusion about which metal is most suitable.

> **Maths skills** Relative values have no units. Relative strength and electrical conductivity are compared with copper here.

....

....

....

.... **(3 marks)**

Extended response – Alloys and corrosion

Some metal cutlery is marked with the letters EPNS. This stands for electroplated nickel silver.

The cutlery itself is made from 'nickel silver', an alloy of nickel, zinc and copper. Electroplating is used to deposit a thin layer of pure silver onto the cutlery. This improves the cutlery's appearance.

Describe how you could electroplate a nickel silver spoon with silver. In your answer, you should name a suitable electrolyte and identify the anode and cathode. You should include half equations to explain the reactions that occur at each electrode.

> When thinking about a suitable electrolyte, it helps to recall that all metal nitrates are soluble in water.

> A simple labelled diagram can save a lot of words when you answer a question like this one.

....

....

....

....

....

....

....

....

....

....

....

....

....

....

....

....

....

....

> You should be able to write half equations for reactions occurring at the anode and cathode in electrolysis.

....

.... **(6 marks)**

Practical skills **Accurate titrations**

1 Suggest a reason that explains why universal indicator solution should **not** be used in titrations.

.... **(1 mark)**

2 An acid–base indicator is used when sodium hydroxide solution is titrated with dilute hydrochloric acid. In this titration, the acid is added to the alkali in a flask. The end-point is when the indicator changes colour.

(a) Name a suitable indicator solution for this titration.

.... **(1 mark)**

(b) Describe the colour change for the indicator named in part (**a**) at the end-point in this titration.

> You need to give the indicator's colour before **and** immediately after the end-point.

.... **(1 mark)**

3 In a titration, it is common to add a 25.0 cm^3 portion of the alkali solution to a conical flask.

Describe how to add 25.0 cm^3 of a liquid to a conical flask accurately and safely for a titration.

I would use a .... *with a* ....

For accuracy, I would .... **(2 marks)**

4 The diagrams show parts of the burette during a titration.

(a) Give the readings to the nearest 0.05 cm^3.

start reading ....

end-point reading .... **(2 marks)**

at start   end-point

(b) Calculate the titre using your answers to part (**a**).

.... **(1 mark)**

5 A student carries out a titration. State why he:

(a) swirls the conical flask containing the alkali solution while adding dilute acid from the burette

.... **(1 mark)**

(b) adds acid drop by drop near the end-point

.... **(1 mark)**

(c) reads the burette at eye level.

.... **(1 mark)**

Concentration calculations

1 Give the following volumes in cubic decimetres, dm^3.

> **Maths skills** Divide by 1000 to convert from cm^3 to dm^3.

(a) $500 \ cm^3$

.... **(1 mark)**

(b) $125 \ cm^3$

.... **(1 mark)**

(c) $25 \ cm^3$

.... **(1 mark)**

2 Calculate the concentrations, in $mol \ dm^{-3}$, of the solutions formed by the following mixtures.

> **Guided**

(a) $0.10 \ mol$ of sodium hydroxide dissolved in $0.25 \ dm^3$ of water.

.... **(1 mark)**

(b) $0.40 \ mol$ of potassium chloride dissolved in $250 \ cm^3$ of water.

$\left(\dfrac{0.40}{250}\right) \times 1000 =$ .... **(1 mark)**

(c) $0.020 \ mol$ of glucose dissolved in $50 \ cm^3$ of water.

.... **(1 mark)**

3 Calculate the concentrations, in $g \ dm^{-3}$, of the following solutions.

> **Guided**

(a) $0.15 \ mol \ dm^{-3}$ of NaOH(aq). (M_r of NaOH = 40)

$0.15 \times 40 =$ .... **(1 mark)**

(b) $0.050 \ mol \ dm^{-3}$ of $AgNO_3$(aq). (M_r of $AgNO_3$ = 170)

.... **(1 mark)**

(c) $0.220 \ mol \ dm^{-3}$ of HCl(aq). (M_r of HCl = 36.5)

.... **(1 mark)**

4 Calculate the concentrations, in $mol \ dm^{-3}$, of the following solutions.

> **Guided**

(a) $4.8 \ g \ dm^{-3}$ of LiOH(aq). (M_r of LiOH = 24)

$\dfrac{4.8}{24} =$ .... **(1 mark)**

(b) $19 \ g \ dm^{-3}$ of $MgCl_2$(aq). (M_r of $MgCl_2$ = 95)

.... **(1 mark)**

(c) $21.0 \ g \ dm^{-3}$ of $CuSO_4$(aq). (M_r of $CuSO_4$ = 159.5)

> **Maths skills** The M_r value is precise to four significant figures but the concentration in $g \ dm^{-3}$ is precise to only three significant figures. The final answer should therefore be given to three significant figures.

.... **(1 mark)**

Titration calculations

1 A student adds dilute hydrochloric acid from a burette to 25.00 cm^3 samples of sodium hydroxide solution in a conical flask. The table shows the results of titrations carried out after her rough titration.

	1st titration	2nd titration	3rd titration
final burette reading (cm^3)	46.30	23.05	45.45
initial burette reading (cm^3)	24.00	0.40	23.05
titre (cm^3)	22.30		

Guided

(a) Calculate the missing titres and complete the table. **(1 mark)**

(b) Titres that are within 0.20 cm^3 of each other are concordant titres. Calculate the mean of the concordant titres from the student's results.

> 🖩 **Maths skills** Make sure your answers are precise to two decimal places, and end in 0 or 5.

....

....

mean = ... **(2 marks)**

2 Sodium hydroxide solution reacts with dilute hydrochloric acid:

$$NaOH(aq) + HCl(aq) \rightarrow NaCl(aq) + H_2O(l)$$

Guided

In a titration, 24.50 cm^3 of dilute hydrochloric acid is needed to neutralise 25.00 cm^3 of 0.100 mol dm^{-3} sodium hydroxide solution. Calculate the concentration of the dilute hydrochloric acid in mol dm^{-3}.

amount of NaOH = $0.100 \times \left(\dfrac{25.00}{1000}\right)$ = ... mol

$1 : 1$ ratio between NaOH and HCl, so amount of HCl = ... mol

concentration of HCl = $\left(\dfrac{............}{24.50}\right) \times 1000$ = ... mol dm^{-3} **(3 marks)**

3 In a titration, 27.50 cm^3 of 0.200 mol dm^{-3} hydrochloric acid is needed to neutralise 25.00 cm^3 of a sodium hydroxide solution. Calculate the concentration of the sodium hydroxide solution in mol dm^{-3}.

....

....

concentration = ... mol dm^{-3} **(3 marks)**

4 Sodium hydroxide solution reacts with dilute sulfuric acid:

$$2NaOH(aq) + H_2SO_4(aq) \rightarrow Na_2SO_4(aq) + 2H_2O(l)$$

In a titration, 31.55 cm^3 of dilute sulfuric acid is needed to neutralise 25.00 cm^3 of 0.400 mol dm^{-3} sodium hydroxide solution. Calculate the concentration of the dilute sulfuric acid in mol dm^{-3}.

> The ratio between the alkali and acid is **not** 1:1 (as it is in questions **2** and **3**).

....

....

....

concentration = ... mol dm^{-3} **(4 marks)**

Percentage yield

1 When it is heated, copper carbonate decomposes to form copper oxide and carbon dioxide. A student heats some copper carbonate. The table shows her results.

Substance	Mass (g)
copper carbonate used	2.5
copper oxide obtained	1.4

What was the actual yield of copper oxide in this experiment?

☐ **A** 1.1 g   ☐ **C** 2.5 g

☐ **B** 1.4 g   ☐ **D** 3.9 g   **(1 mark)**

2 State what is meant by the term **theoretical yield**.

.... **(1 mark)**

3 Magnesium reacts with oxygen to form magnesium oxide: $2Mg(s) + O_2(g) \rightarrow 2MgO(s)$.

A student heats 2.4 g of magnesium in air and obtains 3.0 g of magnesium oxide.

The theoretical yield for this experiment is 4.0 g. The percentage yield is 75%.

〉**Guided**〉 (a) Explain how the percentage yield for this experiment is calculated.

> Give the expression needed to calculate percentage yield, and show how to use it for this experiment.

....

.... **(2 marks)**

(b) The percentage yield in this reaction could be reduced by a side reaction, such as magnesium reacting with nitrogen. Give two other reasons why the percentage yield in this experiment is not 100%.

The reaction might not ....

and some magnesium oxide could be... **(2 marks)**

4 Complete the table to show the missing actual yields, theoretical yields and percentage yields.

> **Maths skills** For experiments C to F, you will need to rearrange the expression for calculating percentage yields.

Experiment	Actual yield (g)	Theoretical yield (g)	Percentage yield (%)
A	45	50	
B	2.43	2.86	
C		50	70
D		3.91	64
E	2.50		50
F	10.4		92

(6 marks)

Atom economy

1 Ethene reacts with steam to form ethanol: $C_2H_4(g) + H_2O(g) \rightarrow CH_3CH_2OH(g)$

What is the atom economy of this reaction?

> Answer D cannot be correct because atom economy cannot be greater than 100%.

☐ **A** 100%

☐ **B** 66.7%

☐ **C** 50%

☐ **D** 150%   **(1 mark)**

2 Potassium nitrate, KNO_3, may be used as a fertiliser. It is manufactured by reacting potassium hydroxide solution with dilute nitric acid:

> **Maths skills** Look at the fourth digit from the left in your answer. Round the third digit up if the fourth digit is 5 or more.

$KOH(aq) + HNO_3(aq) \rightarrow KNO_3(aq) + H_2O(l)$.

Calculate the atom economy of this process. Give your answer to three significant figures.

Guided

(M_r of KNO_3 = 101 and M_r of H_2O = 18)

total M_r of desired product = ...

total M_r of all products = ...

atom economy = $100 \times \dfrac{\text{............}}{\text{............}}$ = ... **(2 marks)**

3 Iron can be extracted from iron(III) oxide by heating with carbon:

$Fe_2O_3(s) + 3C(s) \rightarrow 2Fe(l) + 3CO(g)$

Calculate the atom economy of this process. Give your answer to three significant figures.

(A_r of Fe = 56 and M_r of CO = 28)

> Calculate the **total** A_r and M_r values of the products.

............................% **(2 marks)**

4 Ethanol can be manufactured by fermentation:

glucose → ethanol + carbon dioxide

$C_6H_{12}O_6(aq) \rightarrow 2CH_3CH_2OH(g) + 2CO_2(g)$

(a) Calculate the atom economy of fermentation to produce ethanol. Give your answer to three significant figures. (A_r of H = 1, A_r of C = 12 and A_r of O = 16)

> Calculate the relative formula masses, M_r, of both products first.

............................% **(4 marks)**

(b) Describe one way of improving the atom economy of the process.

....

.... **(1 mark)**

Molar gas volume

1 Hydrogen reacts with chlorine to produce hydrogen chloride gas: $H_2(g) + Cl_2(g) \rightarrow 2HCl(g)$

What is the minimum volume of chlorine gas needed to produce 100 cm^3 of hydrogen chloride?

Assume that the volumes are measured at the same temperature and pressure.

☐ **A** 25 cm^3 ☐ **C** 100 cm^3

☐ **B** 50 cm^3 ☐ **D** 200 cm^3 **(1 mark)**

2 Calculate the volume, in dm^3, of the following amounts of gases at room temperature and pressure.

(molar volume = 24 dm^3)

> **Guided**

(a) 2.0 mol of chlorine, Cl_2.

volume of chlorine = 24 × 2.0 = ... dm^3 **(1 mark)**

(b) 0.50 mol of helium, He.

.... **(1 mark)**

(c) 1.25 mol of ethene, C_2H_4.

.... **(1 mark)**

3 Calculate the amount, in mol, of the following volumes of gases at room temperature and pressure.

(molar volume = 24 000 cm^3)

> **Guided**

(a) 120 cm^3 of hydrogen, H_2

amount of hydrogen = $\dfrac{120}{24\,000}$ = ... mol   **(1 mark)**

(b) 6000 cm^3 of carbon dioxide, CO_2

.... **(1 mark)**

(c) 360 cm^3 of sulfur trioxide, SO_3

.... **(1 mark)**

4 Butane, C_4H_{10}, is one of the fuels used in camping gas. The complete combustion of butane produces carbon dioxide and water vapour:

$C_4H_{10}(g) + 6\frac{1}{2}O_2(g) \rightarrow 4CO_2(g) + 5H_2O(g)$

> Assume that all volumes are measured at the same temperature and pressure. You do **not** need to use molar volume calculations in these two questions.

(a) Calculate the minimum volume of oxygen, O_2, needed to react completely with 400 cm^3 of butane.

.... **(1 mark)**

(b) Calculate the total volume of gaseous products formed in the reaction described in part (**a**).

.... **(1 mark)**

Gas calculations

1 Magnesium reacts with oxygen to form magnesium oxide: $2Mg(s) + O_2(g) \rightarrow 2MgO(s)$

A student strongly heats 2.4 g of magnesium in air. It reacts completely with oxygen.

(a) Calculate the amount, in mol, of magnesium used by the student. (A_r of Mg = 24)

$$\text{amount of Mg} = \frac{2.4}{24} = \text{.......................... mol} \quad \textbf{(1 mark)}$$

(b) (i) Deduce the amount, in mol, of magnesium oxide, MgO, formed in the reaction.

> Look at the ratio of magnesium to magnesium oxide in the balanced equation.

.... **(1 mark)**

(ii) Use your answer to part (**i**) to calculate the mass of MgO formed. (M_r of MgO = 40)

mass of MgO = ...× 40 = ... g **(1 mark)**

(c) (i) Calculate the minimum amount, in mol, of oxygen, O_2, needed to react with the magnesium.

> Look at the ratio of magnesium to oxygen in the balanced equation.

.... **(1 mark)**

(ii) Use your answer to part (**i**) to calculate the minimum volume, in dm^3, of oxygen. (1 mol of any gas occupies 24 dm^3 at room temperature and pressure)

.... **(1 mark)**

2 Sodium reacts with water to form sodium hydroxide and hydrogen:
$2Na(s) + H_2O(g) \rightarrow 2NaOH(aq) + H_2(g)$

A teacher adds 0.30 g of sodium to a trough of water. The sodium reacts completely with the water.

(a) Calculate the amount, in mol, of sodium used by the teacher. (A_r of Na = 23)

.... **(1 mark)**

(b) (i) Deduce the amount, in mol, of sodium hydroxide, NaOH, formed in the reaction.

.... **(1 mark)**

(ii) Use your answer to part (**i**) to calculate the mass of NaOH formed. (M_r of NaOH = 40)

.... **(1 mark)**

(c) (i) Calculate the maximum amount, in mol, of hydrogen, H_2, produced in the reaction.

.... **(1 mark)**

(ii) Use your answer to part (**i**) to calculate the maximum volume, in cm^3, of hydrogen. (1 mol of any gas occupies 24 000 cm^3 at room temperature and pressure)

.... **(1 mark)**

3 Hydrogen and oxygen react together to form water vapour: $2H_2(g) + O_2(g) \rightarrow 2H_2O(g)$

Calculate the maximum mass of water that can be produced from the complete combustion of 1.2 dm^3 of hydrogen at room temperature and pressure. (M_r of H_2O = 18)

.... g **(3 marks)**

Exam skills – Chemical calculations

1   Oxygen is manufactured today by the fractional distillation of liquefied air. It was manufactured in the past using the Brin process. This process happens in two stages:

Stage 1: Barium oxide is heated to 500°C. It reacts with oxygen in the air to form barium peroxide:
$$2BaO(s) + O_2(g) \rightarrow 2BaO_2(s)$$

Stage 2: Barium peroxide is heated to over 800°C, which releases oxygen:
$$2BaO_2(s) \rightarrow 2BaO(s) + O_2(g)$$

Barium oxide formed in stage 2 could then be used again for stage 1.

(a) This part of the question is about stage 1.

> **Maths skills** 1 kg = 1000 g. For example, 5 kg = (5 × 1000) = 5000 g.

  (i) Calculate the amount of barium oxide, in mol, in 250 kg of barium oxide.
  (A_r of Ba = 137 and A_r of O = 16)

  .... **(2 marks)**

  (ii) Calculate the maximum amount, in mol, of oxygen that will react with 250 kg of barium oxide.

  .... **(1 mark)**

  (iii) Calculate the maximum volume, in dm^3, of oxygen that will react with 250 kg of barium oxide.
  Give your answer to three significant figures.
  (1 mol of any gas occupies 24 dm^3 at room temperature and pressure)

  .... **(1 mark)**

(b) Calculate the atom economy of stage 2 of the Brin process for producing oxygen.
Give your answer to two significant figures. (A_r of Ba = 137 and A_r of O = 16)

  .... **(2 marks)**

(c) Carbon dioxide in the air reacts with barium oxide to form barium carbonate. This unwanted side reaction reduces the amount of barium oxide available to react, and so reduces the yield of oxygen.

  (i) Give another reason why the actual yield of oxygen may be less than the theoretical yield.

  .... **(1 mark)**

  (ii) The theoretical yield of oxygen was 26.1 kg but the actual yield was 21.9 kg.
  Calculate the percentage yield.

  .... **(1 mark)**

(d) Barium oxide reacts with water to form barium hydroxide solution:
$$BaO(s) + H_2O(l) \rightarrow Ba(OH)_2(aq)$$

  (i) 2.50 dm^3 of a barium hydroxide solution contains 0.125 mol of barium hydroxide.
  Calculate its concentration in mol/dm^3.

  .... **(1 mark)**

  (ii) Calculate the concentration of the solution in part (**i**) in g/dm^3. (M_r of Ba(OH)$_2$ = 171)

  .... **(1 mark)**

The Haber process

1 In the Haber process, nitrogen and hydrogen react together to form ammonia:

$$N_2(g) + 3H_2(g) \rightleftharpoons 2NH_3(g)$$

(a) What is the raw material for the nitrogen?

☐ **A** air   ☐ **C** seawater

☐ **B** natural gas   ☐ **D** hydrochloric acid   **(1 mark)**

(b) Give the meaning of the symbol $\rightleftharpoons$ in the balanced equation.

.... **(1 mark)**

2 The conditions used in the Haber process are carefully controlled to achieve an acceptable yield of ammonia in an acceptable time.

(a) State the temperature and pressure used in the Haber process.

temperature ....°C

pressure ....atmospheres **(2 marks)**

(b) Explain why iron is used in the Haber
process.

> The reactor is made from steel, and iron is not a reactant or a product.

....

.... **(2 marks)**

3 Dilute ethanoic acid reacts with ethanol. Ethyl
ethanoate and water form in the reaction:

> You may see unfamiliar chemistry in an unfamiliar context, like this one.

$$CH_3COOH(aq) + CH_3CH_2OH(l) \rightleftharpoons CH_3COOCH_2CH_3(aq) + H_2O(l)$$

All four substances are clear, colourless liquids. They mix
completely with each other.

> Do not be put off by the complex appearance of the equation. It is just an example of: $A + B \rightleftharpoons C + D$

(a) State what visible changes, if any, you would observe
during the reaction.

.... **(1 mark)**

Guided (b) The reaction reaches a dynamic equilibrium after a few days.

(i) Describe what is happening to the forward and backward reactions at equilibrium.

The rate of the forward and backward reactions is ....

and they .... **(2 marks)**

(ii) State what happens to the concentrations
of the reacting substances at equilibrium.

> The basic choices you have are: increase, decrease, do not change.

.... **(1 mark)**

More about equilibria

1 The manufacture of sulfuric acid involves a reversible reaction between sulfur dioxide and oxygen:

$$2SO_2(g) + O_2(g) \rightleftharpoons 2SO_3(g) \qquad \text{(forward reaction is exothermic)}$$

(a) Explain the effect of increasing the pressure on the position of equilibrium.

> State what will happen (moves to the left, moves to the right or stays the same), and give a reason why.

....

.... **(2 marks)**

(b) Explain the effect of increasing the temperature on the position of equilibrium.

....

.... **(2 marks)**

(c) State the effect on the position of equilibrium, if the sulfur trioxide is removed.

.... **(1 mark)**

(d) Vanadium(V) oxide, V_2O_5, is used as a catalyst. State the effect of using a catalyst on:

  (i) the position of equilibrium

.... **(1 mark)**

  (ii) the rate of attainment of equilibrium.

.... **(1 mark)**

2 Ammonia is made from nitrogen and hydrogen using the Haber process:

$$N_2(g) + 3H_2(g) \rightleftharpoons 2NH_3(g)$$
(forward reaction is exothermic)

The graph shows how the yield of ammonia depends on the temperature and pressure used.

(a) Identify the temperature and pressure, shown by the graph, needed to obtain the maximum yield.

.... **(1 mark)**

> **Guided**

(b) The conditions chosen are 450°C and 200 atmospheres pressure (atm).

  (i) Identify the percentage yield of ammonia obtained under these conditions, as shown by the graph.

.... **(1 mark)**

  (ii) Explain why these conditions are described as a **compromise** temperature and pressure.

> Mention the position of equilibrium, the rate of reaction and relevant factors such as cost.

Lower temperatures give a ....

but ....

Higher pressures give a ....

but .... **(4 marks)**

Making fertilisers

1 Fertilisers may contain potassium, phosphorus and nitrogen compounds to promote plant growth. Complete the table by placing a tick (✓) to show the elements present in the fertiliser compounds.

Guided

Fertiliser compound	Element required by plants		
	Potassium	**Phosphorus**	**Nitrogen**
NH_4NO_3			✓
$(NH_4)_2SO_4$			
K_3PO_4			
KNO_3			

(3 marks)

2 Ammonium nitrate, NH_4NO_3, is a salt used as a fertiliser. It is made by reacting ammonia solution with dilute nitric acid: $NH_3(aq) + HNO_3(aq) \rightarrow NH_4NO_3(aq)$

Name the type of reaction that produces ammonium nitrate solution.

> Ammonia solution is alkaline.

.... **(1 mark)**

3 Ammonium sulfate, $(NH_4)_2SO_4$, is a salt used as a fertiliser. In the laboratory preparation of ammonium sulfate, ammonia solution is titrated with dilute sulfuric acid.

Guided

(a) Explain why titration is necessary when making a soluble salt such as ammonium sulfate from soluble reactants.

Titration lets you find the correct proportions of .... and ....

to mix together so that the solution contains only .... and .... **(2 marks)**

(b) Describe how you would produce dry crystals of ammonia sulfate from ammonium sulfate solution.

....

....

.... **(3 marks)**

4 The industrial production of ammonium sulfate happens on a much larger scale than the laboratory preparation.

(a) The raw materials for making sulfuric acid are sulfur, air and water.

> These are **not** nitrogen and hydrogen.

Name the raw materials for making ammonia.

.... **(3 marks)**

(b) Suggest reasons that explain why industrial production of ammonium sulfate can be automated, but the laboratory production is difficult to automate.

> What type of process (batch or continuous) does each production method involve?

....

.... **(2 marks)**

Fuel cells

1 The graphs show how the potential difference (voltage) of a chemical cell and fuel cell change during use.

chemical cell

Potential difference (V)

Time (hours)

fuel cell

Potential difference (V)

Time (hours)

> **Guided**

(a) Explain why the voltage of the chemical cell changes in this way.

A chemical cell produces a ....

until .... **(2 marks)**

(b) Explain why the voltage of the fuel cell does not change.

....

.... **(2 marks)**

2 Some electric cars use a hydrogen–oxygen fuel cell. This produces electricity for the electric motor.

> Which gas relevant to fuel cells is found in the air? What does it react with in the fuel cell?

(a) Explain why air must be supplied to the fuel cell.

....

.... **(2 marks)**

(b) Name the only chemical product made by a hydrogen–oxygen fuel cell.

.... **(1 mark)**

3 Some fuel cells use methanol, CH_3OH, for their fuel. When in use, all the carbon atoms are oxidised to carbon dioxide and all the hydrogen atoms are oxidised to water.

Write a balanced equation for the overall reaction that happens in these fuel cells.

.... **(2 marks)**

4 Some electric cars use a rechargeable chemical cell, rather than a hydrogen–oxygen fuel cell, to produce electricity for the electric motor. There were only four public hydrogen filling stations in the UK in 2015.

(a) Explain which type of cell (chemical cell or fuel cell) is likely to be more convenient for use in a car.

....

....

.... **(2 marks)**

(b) Scientists have developed a new design of fuel cell. It uses hydrogen made by the reaction of water with a stored metal hydride powder. Describe two strengths of using this fuel cell for an electric car.

....

....

.... **(2 marks)**

Extended response – Reversible reactions

In the Haber process, nitrogen reacts with hydrogen to produce ammonia. The hydrogen needed is produced from natural gas. This is mostly methane, CH_4. The methane is heated with steam in the presence of a nickel catalyst:

$$CH_4(g) + H_2O(g) \rightleftharpoons CO(g) + 3H_2(g) \qquad \text{(forward reaction is endothermic)}$$

The reaction conditions chosen are a temperature of 950°C and a pressure of 20 atmospheres.

> The reaction is reversible and all the reacting substances are in the gas state.

Evaluate the conditions used in the manufacture of hydrogen using this reaction.

> For an industrial process, the pressure is only moderately high.

> You need to review the information given, including strengths and weaknesses.
>
> You must come to a conclusion supported by the information, and by relevant knowledge and understanding.

....

....

....

....

....

....

....

....

....

....

....

....

....

....

....

....

....

....

> You should be able to explain how the control of the temperature, pressure and catalyst used produces an acceptable yield in an acceptable time. This includes the equilibrium position and the reaction rate.

....

....

....

.... **(6 marks)**

The alkali metals

1 Compared with a typical transition metal such as iron, the alkali metals are:

☐ **A** hard with relatively low melting points   ☐ **C** soft with relatively low melting points

☐ **B** soft with relatively high melting points   ☐ **D** hard with relatively high melting points

(1 mark)

2 Give a reason that explains why, in terms of electronic configurations, the alkali metals occupy group 1.

> The electronic configurations of the atoms of these elements differ, but they do have something in common.

.... **(1 mark)**

3 The alkali metals react with water to produce a metal hydroxide and hydrogen. For example:

sodium + water → sodium hydroxide + hydrogen

Guided

(a) Write the balanced equation for this reaction. Include state symbols.

........Na(......) + ... → ....NaOH(aq) + ... **(3 marks)**

(b) Explain why, during this reaction, the sodium forms a molten ball.

....

.... **(2 marks)**

(c) Describe the chemical test for hydrogen.

....

....

> Make sure that you can recall and apply relevant knowledge and understanding from other topics.

.... **(2 marks)**

4 Explain why lithium, sodium and potassium are stored in oil.

....

.... **(2 marks)**

5 Describe what you would see when a small piece of potassium is added to water.

> You should not name any products in your answer – just write down what you would **see**.

....

....

.... **(3 marks)**

6 Reactivity increases going down group 1, from lithium to potassium. Explain this pattern in reactivity in terms of the electronic configurations of the atoms.

Guided

Going down the group, the size of the atoms ....

....

.... **(3 marks)**

The halogens

1 Which of the following is a chemical test for chlorine gas?

> Answer D cannot be correct because chlorine must dissolve in water for the chemical test to work.

☐ **A** Damp red litmus paper turns blue, then white.

☐ **B** Damp blue litmus paper turns red, then white.

☐ **C** Damp starch iodide paper turns red, then white.

☐ **D** Dry starch iodide paper turns blue–black.   **(1 mark)**

2 Give a reason that explains why, in terms of electronic configurations, the halogens occupy group 7.

.... **(1 mark)**

3 Complete the table to show the colours and physical states of the halogens at room temperature.

Guided

Halogen	Colour	Physical state
chlorine		
bromine		
iodine	dark grey	solid (forms a purple vapour)

(4 marks)

4 The table shows the densities of two halogens, in order going down group 7.

Halogen	Density at room temperature and pressure (kg/m³)
bromine	3103
iodine	4933

Predict the density of astatine, the element placed immediately below iodine, and justify your answer.

....

.... **(2 marks)**

5 Fluorine at the top of group 7 exists as simple molecules. Each molecule contains two fluorine atoms.

(a) Name the type of bond that exists between the atoms in a fluorine molecule.

.... **(1 mark)**

(b) Explain why fluorine has a low boiling point.

> In your answer, make sure that you identify the bonds or forces overcome during boiling.

....

.... **(2 marks)**

(c) Describe and explain the trend in melting point going down group 7.

....

.... **(2 marks)**

Reactions of halogens

1 In the cold and dark, hydrogen reacts explosively with fluorine to produce hydrogen fluoride, HF.

(a) Write a balanced equation for this reaction.

> Remember that the gaseous elements (apart from those in group 0) exist as diatomic molecules, X_2.

.... **(2 marks)**

(b) What happens when hydrogen fluoride is added to water?

☐ **A** It reacts vigorously, releasing oxygen.

☐ **B** It dissolves to form an alkaline solution.

☐ **C** It dissolves to form an acidic solution.

☐ **D** It dissolves to form a neutral salt solution. **(1 mark)**

(c) If exposed to sunlight, a mixture of hydrogen and chlorine reacts explosively. Suggest reasons that explain why a mixture of hydrogen and bromine reacts only if a flame is put in it.

> Look again at the reaction conditions needed for hydrogen with fluorine or chlorine.

....

....

.... **(2 marks)**

2 A teacher heats a small piece of sodium in a steel deflagrating spoon until the sodium ignites. She then puts the spoon in a gas jar of chlorine. The sodium burns in the chlorine to produce sodium chloride.

Guided

(a) Write the balanced equation for this reaction. Include state symbols.

......Na(...) + Cl_2(......) → ......NaCl(......) **(3 marks)**

(b) The teacher then passes bromine vapour over hot iron wool. Red–brown iron(III) bromide, $FeBr_3$, is produced. Write the balanced equation for this reaction.

.... **(2 marks)**

(c) A student places some iron wool in a boiling tube with a few crystals of iodine. He heats the iodine gently to produce iodine vapour, and then heats the iron wool strongly. The iron and iodine react slowly to produce grey iron(II) iodide, FeI_2.

> Make sure that you can recall the formulae of elements, simple compounds and ions.

(i) Write the formula of the iron(II) ion and the formula of the iodide ion.

.... **(2 marks)**

(ii) Write the balanced equation for this reaction.

.... **(2 marks)**

3 Reactivity decreases going down group 7, from fluorine to iodine. Explain, in terms of the electronic configurations of their atom, why fluorine is more reactive than chlorine.

Guided

Fluorine atoms are .... than chlorine atoms ....

....

.... **(3 marks)**

Halogen displacement reactions

1　A student adds a few drops of aqueous bromine solution to a potassium iodide solution. Iodine and potassium bromide solution forms. What type of reaction is this?

> Answer **C** cannot be correct because distillation is a physical separation method, not a chemical reaction.

☐　**A**　neutralisation

☐　**B**　precipitation

☐　**C**　distillation

☐　**D**　redox　　　　　　　**(1 mark)**

2　A displacement reaction may happen when a halogen is added to a solution containing halide ions. The table shows results from an investigation with three halogens. A tick (✓) shows that displacement happens.

Halogen added	Halide ion in solution		
	Chloride	**Bromide**	**Iodide**
chlorine	not done	✓	✓
bromine	✗	not done	✓
iodine	✗	✗	not done

Guided　(a)　Use the results shown in the table to deduce the order of reactivity of these halogens.

The order of reactivity, starting with the most reactive, is ....

.... because chlorine displaces ....

.... but bromine displaces only.............................

Iodine .... **(3 marks)**

(b)　Suggest a reason that explains why three possible experiments were not done in the investigation.

.... **(1 mark)**

(c)　Predict whether iodine will be able to displace astatine from astatide ions. Explain your answer.

....

.... **(2 marks)**

3　Fluorine displaces iodine from potassium iodide solution soaked into filter paper:

> Potassium ions, K⁺, are **spectator ions**. You can leave them out of the ionic equation.

$$F_2(g) + 2KI(aq) \rightarrow 2KF(aq) + I_2(aq)$$

Guided　(a)　Write an ionic equation for this reaction.

$F_2(g)$ + ... **(2 marks)**

(b)　Explain, in terms of the gain or loss of electrons, which substance is:

(i)　oxidised

.... **(2 marks)**

(ii)　reduced

.... **(2 marks)**

The noble gases

1 Which of these properties explains why argon is used as a shield gas during welding?

☐ **A** Argon is inert.

☐ **B** Argon is flammable.

☐ **C** Argon has a low density.

☐ **D** Argon is a good conductor of electricity.   **(1 mark)**

2 Explain why helium is used as a lifting gas for party balloons and airships.

> There are two relevant properties. For each one, explain why it is important for this use of helium.

....

.... **(2 marks)**

3 State, in terms of electronic configurations, why the noble gases occupy group 0 of the period table.

.... **(1 mark)**

4 The table shows some information about the noble gases.

Element	Melting point (°C)
helium	−272
neon	−248
argon	−189
krypton	−157
xenon	−111
radon	−71

> Temperatures with less negative numbers are higher temperatures, so −10°C is warmer than −20°C.

(a) Name the noble gas that has the lowest melting point.

.... **(1 mark)**

(b) Oganesson, Og, was discovered early this century. It is placed in group 0 of the periodic table, immediately below radon. Predict the melting point of oganesson, and explain your answer.

....

.... **(2 marks)**

5 The electronic configuration of He (atomic number 2) is 2.

(a) State the electronic configuration of:

(i) neon (atomic number 10):

.... **(1 mark)**

(ii) argon (atomic number 18):

.... **(1 mark)**

(b) Explain, in terms of their electronic configurations, why the noble gases are unreactive.

....

.... **(2 marks)**

Extended response – Groups

The diagram shows the first five elements in groups 1 and 7 of the periodic table.

Group 1	Group 7
lithium	fluorine
sodium	chlorine
potassium	bromine
rubidium	iodine
caesium	astatine

In 2012, the reaction between caesium and fluorine was filmed for the first time. As predicted, the elements reacted together very violently, producing caesium fluoride:

$$2Cs(s) + F_2(g) \rightarrow 2CsF(s)$$

Explain, in terms of electrons, how caesium and fluorine react together to form caesium fluoride. Explain whether each element is reduced or oxidised, and state why this reaction is very violent.

> Caesium fluoride is an ionic compound, formed when caesium and fluorine form oppositely charged ions.

> The reaction is a redox reaction, in which one element loses electrons and the other element gains electrons.

> What are the trends in reactivity in groups 1 and 7?

....

....

....

....

....

....

....

....

....

....

....

....

....

....

....

....

....

> This question also covers content from Topic 1 (key concepts in chemistry). Remember that this topic is common to Paper 1 and Paper 2, and not just covered in Paper 1.

.... **(6 marks)**

Rates of reaction

1 Magnesium ribbon reacts with dilute hydrochloric acid. Magnesium chloride solution and hydrogen gas are formed. Which of the following changes would cause a decrease in the rate of this reaction?

☐ **A** Use a larger volume of hydrochloric acid.

☐ **B** Dilute the hydrochloric acid with water.

☐ **C** Use warmer dilute hydrochloric acid.

☐ **D** Use magnesium powder instead of ribbon. **(1 mark)**

2 Explain what must happen to reactant particles for a reaction to occur.

....

.... **(2 marks)**

3 (a) Describe the meaning of the term **catalyst**.

> **Guided**

A substance that speeds up a reaction without altering the ....

and is unchanged ....

.... **(3 marks)**

(b) Explain, in terms of energy, how a catalyst increases the rate of a reaction.

....

.... **(2 marks)**

(c) (i) State the name given to a biological catalyst.

.... **(1 mark)**

(ii) Give one example of a commercial use of a biological catalyst.

.... **(1 mark)**

4 Lumps of zinc react with dilute sulfuric acid to form zinc sulfate and hydrogen. Explain, using ideas about reactant particles, why the reaction is faster when the same mass of zinc powder is used.

> Think about the surface area to volume ratio of the lumps and powder.

....

....

.... **(2 marks)**

5 Copper oxide powder reacts with dilute hydrochloric acid to form copper chloride and water.

The reaction happens faster if the dilute hydrochloric acid is warmed up before adding the powder.

> You need to think about the energy of collisions as well as their frequency.

Explain, using ideas about reactant particles, why this happens.

....

....

.... **(3 marks)**

Practical skills Investigating rates

1   Sodium thiosulfate solution and dilute hydrochloric acid are clear, colourless solutions. They react together to form sodium chloride solution, water, sulfur dioxide and sulfur:

$$Na_2S_2O_3(aq) + 2HCl(aq) \rightarrow 2NaCl(aq) + H_2O(l) + SO_2(g) + S(s)$$

(a)   Suggest reasons that explain why the production of sodium chloride solution or water **cannot** easily be used to determine the rate of reaction.

....

.... **(2 marks)**

(b)   Sulfur dioxide is a gas that is highly soluble in water.

    (i)   Give one way in which the volume of a gas can be measured accurately.

....**(1 mark)**

    (ii)   Explain why measuring sulfur dioxide is **not** a reliable way to determine the rate of this reaction.

....

.... **(2 marks)**

2   A student investigates how changes in the concentration affect the rate of the reaction between sodium thiosulfate solution and dilute hydrochloric acid. She uses the method shown in the diagram.

The student varies the concentration of sodium thiosulfate solution by diluting it with water. She uses 5 cm³ of 2.0 mol dm⁻³ hydrochloric acid each time. The table shows her results.

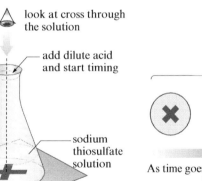

look at cross through the solution

add dilute acid and start timing

sodium thiosulfate solution

view through solution

As time goes on, the solution gets more cloudy. The cross 'disappears'.

Volume of 0.20 mol dm⁻³ Na₂S₂O₃(aq) (cm³)	Volume of water added (cm³)	Concentration of Na₂S₂O₃(aq) added (mol dm⁻³)	Time taken for cross on paper to disappear (s)	Relative rate of reaction, 1000 ÷ time (/s)
10	40	0.04	125	
30	20	0.12	42	24
50	0	0.20	25	

(a)   Describe how the student controls the volume of sodium thiosulfate used in each experiment.

> Study the volumes of sodium thiosulfate solution and water given in the table.

....**(1 mark)**

(b)   Complete the table to show the relative rate of each reaction.   **(2 marks)**

(c)   Describe the relationship between the relative rate of reaction and the concentration of Na₂S₂O₃(aq).

....

.... **(2 marks)**

Exam skills – Rates of reaction

1 A student investigates the rate of reaction between calcium carbonate and dilute hydrochloric acid. He adds some small lumps of calcium carbonate to an excess of acid in a flask, and measures the change in mass. The table shows the student's results.

Time (s)	Change in mass (g)
0	0.00
20	0.48
40	0.76
60	0.88
80	0.94
100	0.96
120	0.96

(a) Plot a graph of change in mass against time using the grid. **(3 marks)**

> Use × or + for each point, and draw a single line of best fit. The line does not have to be a straight line.

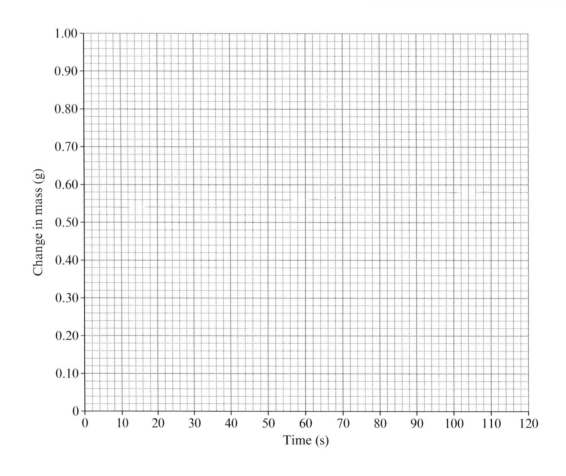

(b) Describe how the student can tell from his results that the reaction has finished.

....

.... **(1 mark)**

(c) The student repeats the experiment. He keeps all the conditions the same, but uses the same starting mass of **powdered** calcium carbonate. On the grid, draw the line that the student should obtain for this experiment.

> You do not need to plot individual points for this line.

Label this line **C**. **(2 marks)**

Heat energy changes

1 Breaking bonds and making bonds involves energy transfers. Which row (**A**, **B**, **C** or **D**) in the table correctly describes these processes?

	Bond breaking	Bond making
☐ **A**	exothermic	exothermic
☐ **B**	exothermic	endothermic
☐ **C**	endothermic	exothermic
☐ **D**	endothermic	endothermic

(1 mark)

2 Describe, in terms of energy transfers, the difference between an exothermic process and an endothermic process.

> Think about whether heat energy is taken in or given out in these processes.

In an exothermic change or reaction, heat energy is ....

but in an endothermic change or reaction, heat energy is .... **(2 marks)**

3 Changes in heat energy occur when salts dissolve in water. They also occur in precipitation reactions.

(a) Magnesium nitrate solution reacts with sodium carbonate solution. Sodium nitrate solution and a precipitate of magnesium carbonate form. The temperature of the reaction mixture decreases.

State whether the reaction is exothermic or endothermic.

.... **(1 mark)**

(b) Give two types of reaction, which take place in aqueous solution, that are always exothermic.

....

.... **(2 marks)**

4 Magnesium reacts with dilute hydrochloric acid, forming magnesium chloride solution and hydrogen gas.

> You should be able to recall the formulae of elements and simple compounds.

(a) Write the balanced equation, including the state symbols, for this reaction.

.... **(3 marks)**

(b) Describe the measurements you would take to confirm that the reaction is exothermic.

> Outline what you would measure, the measuring apparatus and how you would use the results

....

....

.... **(3 marks)**

(c) Explain, in terms of breaking bonds and making bonds, why this reaction is exothermic.

....

....

.... **(3 marks)**

Reaction profiles

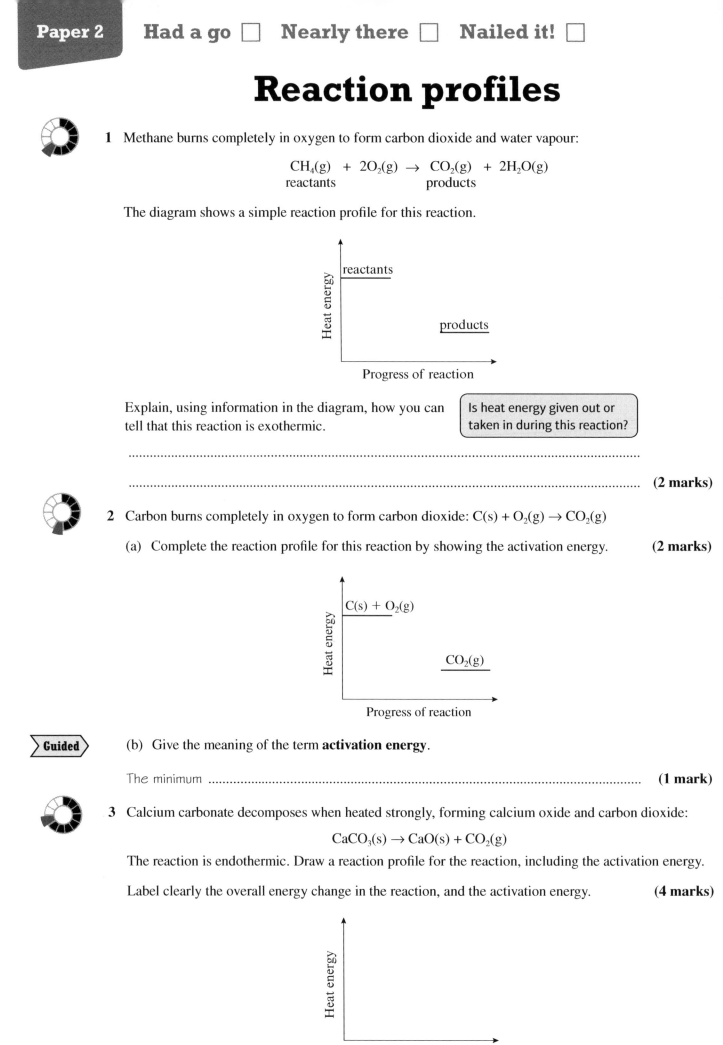

1   Methane burns completely in oxygen to form carbon dioxide and water vapour:

$$CH_4(g) + 2O_2(g) \rightarrow CO_2(g) + 2H_2O(g)$$
reactants   products

The diagram shows a simple reaction profile for this reaction.

Explain, using information in the diagram, how you can tell that this reaction is exothermic.

Is heat energy given out or taken in during this reaction?

....

.... **(2 marks)**

2   Carbon burns completely in oxygen to form carbon dioxide: $C(s) + O_2(g) \rightarrow CO_2(g)$

(a) Complete the reaction profile for this reaction by showing the activation energy.   **(2 marks)**

Guided

(b) Give the meaning of the term **activation energy**.

The minimum .... **(1 mark)**

3   Calcium carbonate decomposes when heated strongly, forming calcium oxide and carbon dioxide:

$$CaCO_3(s) \rightarrow CaO(s) + CO_2(g)$$

The reaction is endothermic. Draw a reaction profile for the reaction, including the activation energy.

Label clearly the overall energy change in the reaction, and the activation energy.   **(4 marks)**

Calculating energy changes

1 Hydrogen and chlorine react together to form hydrogen chloride. The reaction can be modelled using the structures of the molecules involved:

$$H–H + Cl–Cl \rightarrow 2(H–Cl)$$

The table shows the bond energies for the bonds present in the reactants and products.

Bond	H–H	Cl–Cl	H–Cl
Bond energy (kJ mol^{-1})	436	243	432

Guided

(a) Calculate the energy taken in when the bonds in the reactants are broken.

$(1 \times 436) + (1 \times 243) =$ ....kJ mol^{-1} **(1 mark)**

Guided

(b) Calculate the energy given out when the bonds in the products are formed.

$(2 \times 432) =$ ....kJ mol^{-1} **(1 mark)**

Guided

(c) Use your answers to (**a**) and (**b**) to calculate the energy change in the reaction.

energy change = (energy in) − (energy out) = ...

....kJ mol^{-1} **(2 marks)**

(d) Explain, using your answer to (**c**), whether the reaction is exothermic or endothermic.

> The energy change is negative for an exothermic reaction.

....

.... **(2 marks)**

2 In the Haber process, nitrogen and hydrogen react together to produce ammonia. The reaction can be modelled using the structures of the molecules involved:

$$N \equiv N + 3[H—H] \longrightarrow 2 \begin{bmatrix} & H & \\ & | & \\ & N & \\ H & & H \end{bmatrix}$$

The table shows the bond energies for the bonds present in the reactants and products.

Bond	N≡N	H–H	N–H
Bond energy (kJ mol^{-1})	945	436	391

Calculate the energy change for the Haber process.

> Remember to include **all** the N–H bonds present.

...................................kJ mol^{-1} **(4 marks)**

Had a go ☐ Nearly there ☐ Nailed it! ☐

Crude oil

1 Crude oil is described as mainly a complex mixture of:

☐ **A** hydrogen and carbon

☐ **B** alkenes

☐ **C** polymers

☐ **D** hydrocarbons **(1 mark)**

2 Crude oil is a **finite** resource. Explain what this means.

....

.... **(2 marks)**

3 The diagram shows the structures of hexane and cyclohexane, two substances found in crude oil.

hexane

cyclohexane

(a) Write the molecular formula for hexane.

.... **(1 mark)**

> **Guided** >

(b) Explain why hexane and cyclohexane are hydrocarbons.

They are compounds of ....

.... **(2 marks)**

4 Crude oil is an important source of fuels. Octane, C_8H_{18}, is a substance obtained from crude oil that is used as a fuel.

(a) Write a balanced equation for the complete combustion of octane in oxygen.

> The only products are carbon dioxide and water.

.... **(2 marks)**

(b) Describe the chemical test for carbon dioxide.

> State what you would do and what you would observe.

....

.... **(2 marks)**

5 Crude oil is an important feedstock for the petrochemical industry. For example, poly(chloroethene) or PVC is a polymer made from chloroethene. The chloroethene itself is made in two stages from ethene, a substance produced from crude oil.

Explain the meaning of the term **feedstock**.

....

.... **(2 marks)**

Fractional distillation

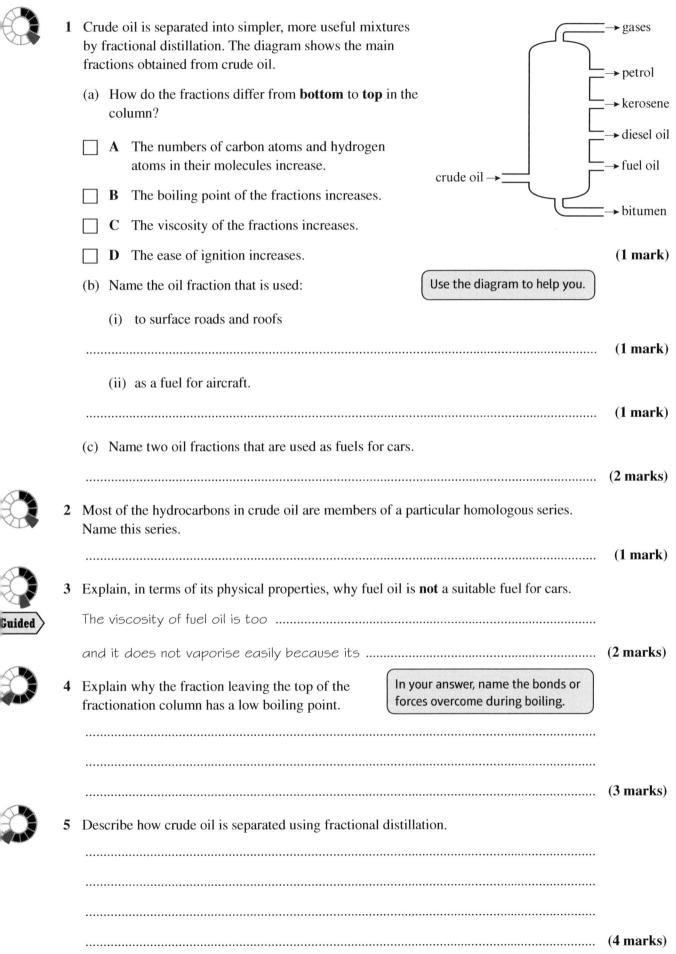

1 Crude oil is separated into simpler, more useful mixtures by fractional distillation. The diagram shows the main fractions obtained from crude oil.

(a) How do the fractions differ from **bottom** to **top** in the column?

   ☐ **A**   The numbers of carbon atoms and hydrogen atoms in their molecules increase.

   ☐ **B**   The boiling point of the fractions increases.

   ☐ **C**   The viscosity of the fractions increases.

   ☐ **D**   The ease of ignition increases.   **(1 mark)**

(b) Name the oil fraction that is used:

> Use the diagram to help you.

   (i)   to surface roads and roofs

.... **(1 mark)**

   (ii)   as a fuel for aircraft.

.... **(1 mark)**

(c) Name two oil fractions that are used as fuels for cars.

.... **(2 marks)**

2 Most of the hydrocarbons in crude oil are members of a particular homologous series. Name this series.

.... **(1 mark)**

3 Explain, in terms of its physical properties, why fuel oil is **not** a suitable fuel for cars.

Guided   The viscosity of fuel oil is too ....

and it does not vaporise easily because its .... **(2 marks)**

4 Explain why the fraction leaving the top of the fractionation column has a low boiling point.

> In your answer, name the bonds or forces overcome during boiling.

....

....

.... **(3 marks)**

5 Describe how crude oil is separated using fractional distillation.

....

....

....

.... **(4 marks)**

Alkanes

1 Natural gas is a hydrocarbon fuel. It is mainly methane, CH_4. Which of the following substances cannot be released when methane burns in air?

☐ **A** water ☐ **C** hydrogen

☐ **B** carbon ☐ **D** carbon dioxide **(1 mark)**

2 The alkanes form an homologous series of hydrocarbons.

 Guided

(a) State the general formula for the alkanes.

C_nH .... **(1 mark)**

(b) Dodecane is an alkane that has 12 carbon atoms in its molecules.

(i) Predict the molecular formula of dodecane.

.... **(1 mark)**

(ii) Name the products of complete combustion of dodecane.

> These products will be the same, whichever alkane undergoes complete combustion.

.... **(2 marks)**

(iii) State why complete combustion of alkanes involves oxidation.

.... **(1 mark)**

3 Similar to the alkanes, the alcohols form an homologous series of compounds. The table shows information about the first three members of the alcohol homologous series.

Name of alcohol	Molecular formula	Structure
methanol	CH_4O	H | H—C—O—H | H
ethanol	C_2H_6O	H H | | H—C—C—O—H | | H H
propanol	C_3H_8O	H H H | | | H—C—C—C—O—H | | | H H H

(a) Give two ways in which the molecules of methanol, ethanol and propanol are similar to each other.

....

.... **(2 marks)**

(b) State how the molecular formula of an alcohol differs from its neighbouring compounds.

> Compare the three molecular formulae. It may also help to compare the three structures.

.... **(1 mark)**

Incomplete combustion

1 Petrol is a hydrocarbon fuel. When it burns in air, waste products form and energy is transferred to the surroundings. Which row in the table correctly shows differences when 1 dm³ of petrol undergoes complete combustion or incomplete combustion?

	Complete combustion	Incomplete combustion
☐ A	more energy transferred	water vapour produced
☐ B	more energy transferred	water vapour not produced
☐ C	water vapour produced	more energy transferred
☐ D	water vapour not produced	more energy transferred

(1 mark)

2 When diesel oil burns in a limited supply of air, carbon monoxide gas and carbon particles are produced.

Guided

(a) Explain why carbon monoxide is toxic.

When breathed in, carbon monoxide combines with ....

so .... (2 marks)

(b) Give a reason that explains why carbon particles may be harmful to health if breathed in.

.... (1 mark)

3 The diagram shows a bird's nest blocking the pipes leading to and from a central heating boiler.

Explain how the nest affects the safety of the people who live in the house.

....

....

....

....

(3 marks)

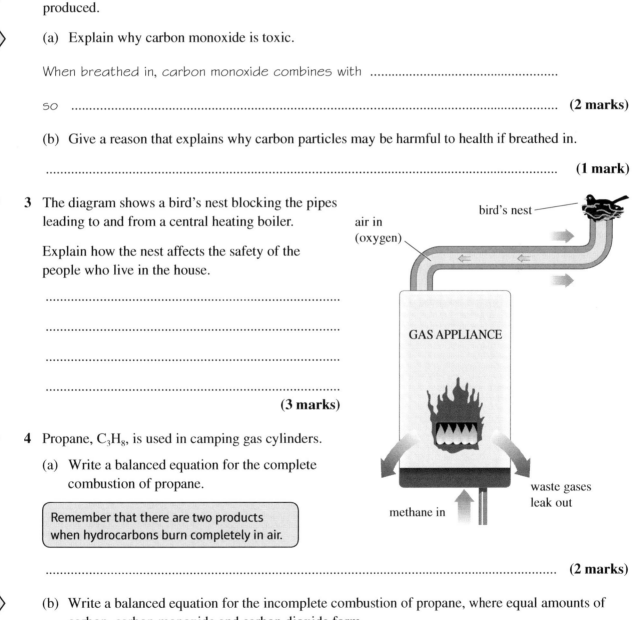

bird's nest

air in (oxygen)

GAS APPLIANCE

methane in

waste gases leak out

4 Propane, C_3H_8, is used in camping gas cylinders.

(a) Write a balanced equation for the complete combustion of propane.

> Remember that there are two products when hydrocarbons burn completely in air.

.... (2 marks)

Guided

(b) Write a balanced equation for the incomplete combustion of propane, where equal amounts of carbon, carbon monoxide and carbon dioxide form.

C_3H_8 + ...O_2 → ....H_2O + ... + ... + ... (2 marks)

Acid rain

Guided

1 Nitrogen and oxygen can react together to form nitrogen dioxide, NO_2, which is a pollutant gas.

(a) Write a balanced equation for this reaction.

....

> Remember that elements that are gases at room temperature (apart from the noble gases) exist as diatomic molecules, X_2.

.... **(2 marks)**

(b) Explain why oxides of nitrogen, such as nitrogen dioxide, are produced by working engines.

Oxygen and nitrogen from ....

react together at the high .... **(2 marks)**

(c) Many fuels used in engines contain impurities that cause the formation of another pollutant gas, which is acidic.

(i) Name the element present in these impurities that produces this gas.

.... **(1 mark)**

(ii) Describe, with the help of a balanced equation, how the element named in part (**i**) causes the formation of this gas.

....

.... **(2 mark)**

Guided

2 Sulfur dioxide dissolves in rainwater to produce an acidic solution. Write a balanced equation to show the reaction that forms dilute sulfurous acid, H_2SO_3. Include state symbols.

SO_2(........) + ...(........) → ....(........)　　　　　**(2 marks)**

3 Acid rain forms when sulfur dioxide dissolves in rainwater.

(a) The diagrams show two old gravestones. The one on the left is made from marble, and the other is made from granite. Explain why they are evidence for acid rain in the area.

> Marble contains calcium carbonate, $CaCO_3$, but granite does not.

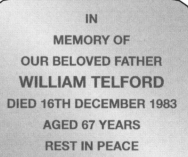

IN
MEMORY OF
OUR BELOVED FATHER
WILLIAM TELFORD
DIED 16TH DECEMBER 1983
AGED 67 YEARS
REST IN PEACE

....

.... **(2 marks)**

(b) Describe two problems, other than the one shown in part (**a**), caused by acid rain.

....

.... **(2 marks)**

Choosing fuels

1 Crude oil and natural gas are finite resources because they take a very long time to form, or are no longer being made. Methane is a non-renewable fossil fuel that is found in natural gas.

> Non-renewable and finite have different meanings. Do not answer by writing 'it is not renewable'.

State why methane is described as **non-renewable**.

.... **(1 mark)**

2 Petrol, kerosene and diesel oil are fossil fuels.

(a) State the name of the substance from which these fuels are obtained.

.... **(1 mark)**

(b) Give one example of how each fuel is used.

Petrol is used as a fuel for cars. Kerosene is used as a fuel for...............................

.... **(2 marks)**

3 Hydrogen and petrol may both be used as fuels for cars.

(a) Write the balanced equation for the reaction between hydrogen and oxygen.

> There is only one product.

.... **(2 marks)**

(b) Petrol is a complex mixture of hydrocarbons. Name one product of the complete combustion of petrol that is **not** produced when hydrogen burns.

.... **(1 mark)**

4 The table shows some information about hydrogen and petrol.

Fuel	Energy released by 1 kg of fuel (MJ)	State at room temperature and pressure	Volume of 1 kg at room temperature and pressure (dm^3)
hydrogen	141.8	gas	12000
petrol	47.3	liquid	1.36

(a) Calculate, to 3 significant figures, the volume of hydrogen needed to release 100 MJ of energy.

$$\text{Volume needed} = 12\,000 \times \left(\frac{120}{24\,000}\right) = \text{.....................} \ dm^3 \quad \textbf{(1 mark)}$$

(b) Calculate, to three significant figures, the volume of petrol needed to release 100 MJ of energy.

.... **(1 mark)**

(c) Using information in the table and your answers to (a) and (b):

(i) identify an advantage of using hydrogen rather than petrol as a fuel for cars.

.... **(1 mark)**

(ii) identify an advantage of using petrol rather than hydrogen as a fuel for cars.

.... **(1 mark)**

Cracking

1 Alkanes and alkenes form two different homologous series. Which row in the table correctly describes each type of hydrocarbon?

	Alkanes	Alkenes
☐ **A**	saturated	contain only C–H and C–C bonds
☐ **B**	unsaturated	contain only C–H and C–C bonds
☐ **C**	contain only C–H and C–C bonds	saturated
☐ **D**	contain only C–H and C–C bonds	unsaturated

(1 mark)

2 In the diagram below, a cracking reaction is modelled using the structures of the molecules.

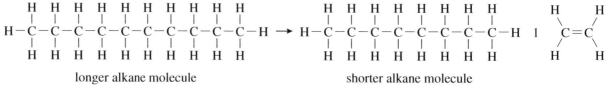

longer alkane molecule   shorter alkane molecule

(a) Name the **type** of hydrocarbon shown by the smallest molecule above.

.... **(1 mark)**

(b) Write the balanced equation, using molecular formulae, for this cracking reaction.

> Count the carbon atoms and hydrogen atoms in each molecule to work out the formulae needed.

.... **(2 marks)**

3 Explain what is meant by **cracking**.

Guided

A reaction in which larger alkanes are broken down into ....

.... **(2 marks)**

4 Crude oil is separated into more useful mixtures called fractions by fractional distillation.

(a) Explain why an oil refinery may crack the fractions containing larger alkanes.

....

.... **(2 marks)**

(b) The graphs show the composition of crude oil obtained from two different oil wells.

Explain why oil from one of the oil wells is probably **not** sent for cracking.

....

.... **(2 marks)**

Extended response – Fuels

Camping gas is a mixture of propane and butane, obtained from crude oil. It is a rainy day and some campers are making tea inside their tent. Incomplete combustion of the camping gas could occur if the campers do not take adequate precautions.

> How does incomplete combustion occur?

Explain how incomplete combustion of hydrocarbons such as propane and butane occurs, and the problems that it can cause in a situation similar to this one. You may include a balanced equation in your answer.

> Which is a more efficient use of fuels, complete or incomplete combustion, and why does this matter?

> What are the products of the incomplete combustion of hydrocarbons? What problems do they cause?

....

....

....

....

....

....

....

....

....

....

....

....

....

.... **(6 marks)**

> Carbon dioxide may be produced during incomplete combustion as well as during complete combustion, and so does not explain the problems that this gas causes.

The early atmosphere

1 From where did the gases that formed the Earth's earliest atmosphere come?

☐ **A** combustion   ☐ **C** photosynthesis

☐ **B** volcanic activity   ☐ **D** condensation   **(1 mark)**

2 The table shows possible percentages of four gases in the Earth's early atmosphere.

Name of gas	Percentage in atmosphere
nitrogen	trace amount
oxygen	trace amount
water vapour	75
carbon dioxide	14

(a) Name the most abundant gas in the modern atmosphere.

It is one of the four gases shown in the table.

.... **(1 mark)**

(b) Explain how the Earth's oceans formed.

....

.... **(2 marks)**

(c) The Earth's atmosphere today contains about 0.04% carbon dioxide. Explain how the oceans contributed to the change in the percentage of carbon dioxide in the atmosphere.

....

.... **(2 marks)**

3 Describe the chemical test for oxygen.

Write down what you would do and what you would observe.

....

.... **(2 marks)**

4 The Earth's atmosphere today contains more oxygen than its early atmosphere did.

In your answer, include the name of the process involved.

> **Guided**

Explain why the percentage of oxygen in the atmosphere has gradually increased.

The growth of primitive plants..

....

.... **(3 marks)**

5 Different teams of scientists may give different percentages for the various gases in the Earth's early atmosphere. Suggest a reason that explains why this happens.

.... **(1 mark)**

Greenhouse effect

1 Carbon dioxide and water vapour are described as greenhouse gases.

   (a) Name another greenhouse gas, often released as a result of livestock farming.

   .... **(1 mark)**

   (b) The use of fossil fuels increases the concentration of carbon dioxide in the atmosphere.

   > What type of substance is found in fossil fuels such as petrol? What happens when they are burned?

   (i) Explain why the use of fossil fuels causes the release of carbon dioxide.

   ....

   .... **(2 marks)**

   (ii) Explain why the release of carbon dioxide from recent human activities, such as using fuels, is causing an increase in the concentration of carbon dioxide in the atmosphere.

   > What processes release carbon dioxide to the atmosphere and remove it, and how fast do they work?

   ....

   ....

   .... **(3 marks)**

2 Explain what is meant by the **greenhouse effect**.

Guided

   Various gases in the atmosphere, such as carbon dioxide, absorb ....

   .... *and then release* ....

   which .... **(3 marks)**

3 The graph shows how the mean global temperature, and the percentage of carbon dioxide in the atmosphere, have changed over the last 220 000 years.

   — difference in temperature

   ▓ percentage of CO_2 in the air

   200 1850 100 50 0
   Thousands of years before today

   (a) Suggest a reason that explains why these measurements may not be certain.

   ....

   .... **(1 mark)**

   (b) Describe the relationship between the carbon dioxide level and global temperature, shown in the graph.

   ....

   .... **(2 marks)**

   (c) State an environmental effect of increasing mean global temperatures.

   .... **(1 mark)**

Extended response – Atmospheric science

The graph shows the change in mean global temperature, and the concentration of carbon dioxide in the atmosphere, between the years 1850 and 2005.

A higher temperature than the mean temperature gives a positive temperature change on the graph.

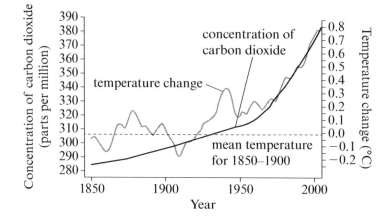

Evaluate whether these graphs provide evidence that human activity is causing the Earth's temperature to increase. In your answer, explain how carbon dioxide acts as a greenhouse gas, and describe processes that release or remove carbon dioxide.

....

....

....

....

....

....

....

....

....

....

....

....

....

....

....

....

....

You should be able to evaluate evidence for human activity causing climate change. This could include correlations between the change in atmospheric carbon dioxide concentration, the consumption of fossil fuels and temperature change.

.... **(6 marks)**

Tests for metal ions

1 Complete the table by writing the flame test colour expected for each ion.

Metal ion	calcium Ca^{2+}	copper Cu^{2+}	lithium Li^+	potassium K^+	sodium Na^+
Flame test colour					yellow

(4 marks)

2 A student carries out a flame test on a sample of sodium chloride. This is the method that she uses:

Method

- Open the Bunsen burner air hole half-way to get a flame that is neither luminous nor roaring.
- Dip a clean wire loop into hydrochloric acid, and then into the sample.
- Put the tip of the wire loop into the edge of the flame and record the flame colour.

(a) Suggest a reason that explains why platinum is a suitable metal to use for the flame test loop.

🧪 **Practical skills** The test for any ion must be unique and the results not mistaken for those of any other ion.

....

.... **(1 mark)**

(b) Suggest a reason that explains why the flame must not be a luminous flame (the orange 'safety flame').

.... **(1 mark)**

3 Dilute sodium hydroxide solution can be used to identify some metal ions in solution. Different metal ions produce different coloured metal hydroxide precipitates.

(a) A student adds a few drops of sodium hydroxide solution to a sample of copper chloride solution.

(i) State the colour of the precipitate formed in the test.

.... **(1 mark)**

(ii) Write a balanced ionic equation for the reaction that produces the precipitate.

$Cu^{2+}(aq) + ... OH^-(......) \rightarrow Cu(OH)_2(.......)$ **(2 marks)**

(b) Describe how you would distinguish between iron(II) sulfate solution and iron(III) sulfate solution using this test.

You do not need to describe the test, only the results for the two solutions.

....

.... **(2 marks)**

(c) Calcium hydroxide and aluminium hydroxide are both white. Describe how you would distinguish between them.

....

.... **(2 marks)**

More tests for ions

1. Some halide ions can be identified using silver nitrate solution. Different coloured silver halide precipitates form.

(a) Complete the table by writing the colour expected for the precipitate.

Silver halide	AgCl	AgBr	AgI
Precipitate colour	white		

(2 marks)

(b) The sample should be acidified using dilute nitric acid. Explain why the sample should **not** be acidified using dilute hydrochloric acid instead.

....

.... (2 marks)

2. Carbonate ions, CO_3^{2-}, can be identified by adding dilute acid to the sample.

(a) State the observation expected in this test.

.... (1 mark)

(b) Describe a test to confirm the results seen in your answer to part (a).

> Describe a test for a particular gas – write down what you would do and what you would see.

....

.... (2 marks)

3. Sulfate ions, SO_4^{2-}, can be identified by adding barium chloride solution to the sample.

(a) State the observation expected in this test.

.... (1 mark)

(b) Explain why the sample must be acidified with dilute hydrochloric acid for this test.

> Barium carbonate is a white, insoluble solid.

....

.... (2 marks)

4. Ammonium ions, NH_4^+, can be identified by adding dilute sodium hydroxide solution to the sample, and then warming the mixture.

(a) Name the gas produced in this test.

.... (1 mark)

(b) Describe the chemical test for the gas produced in this test.

> Write down what you would do and what you would see.

....

.... (2 marks)

Instrumental methods

1   Several instrumental methods of chemical analysis are available.

Describe three ways in which instrumental methods of analysis improve chemical tests.

1   ....

2   ....

3   .... **(3 marks)**

2   The emission spectra on the right were produced by flame photometry.

(a)   The mix contains two different metal ions.

    (i)   Explain how you can tell that the mix does **not** contain lithium ions.

> Which lines are present in the spectrum for lithium ions? Are these present in the spectrum for the mix?

....

....

.... **(2 marks)**

    (ii)   Identify the formulae of the ions present in the mix.

.... **(2 marks)**

Guided

(b)   Describe how you could use emission spectra to identify an ion in an unknown solution.

Obtain the reference spectra for different ions, then ....

....

.... **(2 marks)**

3   Data from the flame photometer can be used to determine the concentration of ions in dilute solution. The diagram shows a calibration curve for potassium ions in solution.

Deduce the concentration of potassium ions that gives a reading of 25%.

.... mol dm^{-3} **(1 mark)**

Practical skills Extended response – Tests for ions

The labels have come off four storage bottles:

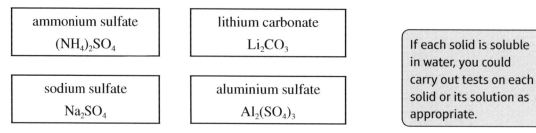

| ammonium sulfate $(NH_4)_2SO_4$ | lithium carbonate Li_2CO_3 |
| sodium sulfate Na_2SO_4 | aluminium sulfate $Al_2(SO_4)_3$ |

> If each solid is soluble in water, you could carry out tests on each solid or its solution as appropriate.

Each bottle contains a different white crystalline solid. Each solid is soluble in water.

Explain how, using chemical tests, you could identify which substances each bottle contains.

> There may be more than one way to distinguish between these four compounds, so think carefully about how to apply your knowledge and understanding in a logical way. Make sure that you outline what you would do, what you would observe and how you would use these observations.

....

....

....

....

....

....

....

....

....

....

....

....

....

....

....

....

....

> You should be able to identify the ions in unknown salts using any of the chemical tests in the Specification.

....

....

....

.... **(6 marks)**

More about alkanes

1 The diagram shows the structure of a molecule of propane.

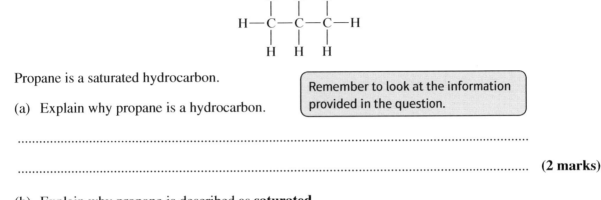

Propane is a saturated hydrocarbon.

Remember to look at the information provided in the question.

(a) Explain why propane is a hydrocarbon.

....

.... **(2 marks)**

(b) Explain why propane is described as **saturated**.

Propane does not contain ....;

it contains only .... **(2 marks)**

2 The table shows some information about some alkanes. Complete the table.

Name of alkane	Molecular formula	Structure
	CH_4	H—C—H with H above and H below
ethane		H—C—C—H structure with H atoms
butane	C_4H_{10}	

(3 marks)

3 Pentane, C_5H_{12}, is an alkane found in petrol. It undergoes complete combustion in excess oxygen.

(a) Name the products formed by the complete combustion of pentane.

.... **(2 marks)**

(b) Write a balanced equation for the complete combustion of pentane.

C_5H_{12} + ... O_2 → .... + ... **(2 marks)**

(c) Diesel oil contains hexadecane, an alkane with 16 carbon atoms in its molecules. Deduce its molecular formula.

What is the general formula for the alkanes? Look at the table in question **2** to see the pattern.

....

.... **(1 mark)**

Alkenes

1   The diagram shows the structure of a molecule of ethene.

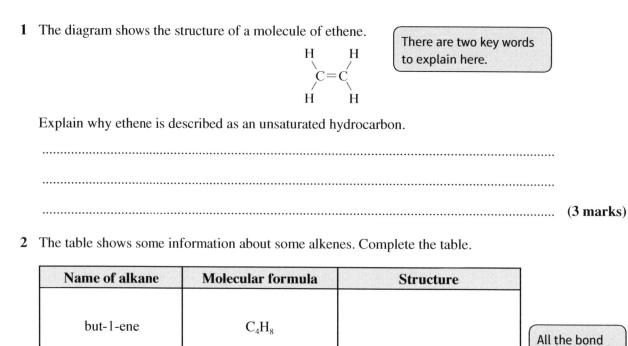

> There are two key words to explain here.

Explain why ethene is described as an unsaturated hydrocarbon.

....

....

.... **(3 marks)**

2   The table shows some information about some alkenes. Complete the table.

Name of alkane	Molecular formula	Structure
but-1-ene	C_4H_8	
but-2-ene		H—C—C=C—C (with H atoms)

> All the bond angles can be 90° if you find this easier to draw.

(2 marks)

3   Propene, C_3H_6, is an alkene that undergoes complete combustion in excess oxygen.

> Guided

(a)   Write a balanced equation for the complete combustion of propene.

C_3H_6 + ... O_2 → .... + ...   **(2 marks)**

(b)   Octadecene is an alkene with 18 carbon atoms in its molecules. Deduce its molecular formula.

> What is the general formula for the alkenes?

.... **(1 mark)**

4   Alkenes undergo addition reactions with bromine and bromine water.

> Write down what you would do and what you would observe for hexane and for hexene.

Describe a chemical test to distinguish between the liquids hexane and hexene.

....

....

.... **(3 marks)**

Addition polymers

1 State the meaning of the term **polymer**.

A substance of high average ....

made up of small .... **(2 marks)**

2 Ethene molecules, C_2H_4, can combine in a polymerisation reaction.

(a) State the type of polymerisation reaction involved.

.... **(1 mark)**

(b) State the feature of ethene molecules that allows them to take part in this reaction.

.... **(1 mark)**

(c) Name the polymer formed in the reaction.

.... **(1 mark)**

3 The diagram shows the repeating unit of a polymer.

Draw the structure of a molecule of the monomer that was used to produce this polymer.

$$\left[\begin{array}{c} H \quad\; H \\ | \quad\; | \\ -C-C- \\ | \quad\; | \\ H \;\; CH_3 \end{array}\right]$$

(1 mark)

4 The diagram shows the structure of a molecule of tetrafluoroethene, C_2F_4.

Explain how these molecules form poly(tetrafluoroethene), also called PTFE.

$$\begin{array}{c} F \qquad F \\ \backslash \qquad / \\ C=C \\ / \qquad \backslash \\ F \qquad F \end{array}$$

You may use an equation as part of your answer.

> Chemical reactions involve bond breaking and bond making. Which bonds break and which bonds form?

....

....

....

....

.... **(3 marks)**

5 Poly(chloroethene), also called PVC, is a component of electrical cables. Explain how the properties of PVC make it suitable for this use.

> Mention the two most important properties only, and why they make PVC suitable for an electrical cable.

....

....

.... **(2 marks)**

Condensation polymers

1 (a) The diagram shows the structure of propane-1,3-diol.

$$H-O-\underset{\underset{H}{|}}{\overset{\overset{H}{|}}{C}}-\underset{\underset{H}{|}}{\overset{\overset{H}{|}}{C}}-\underset{\underset{H}{|}}{\overset{\overset{H}{|}}{C}}-O-H$$

Identify an alcohol functional group by drawing a circle around it on the diagram. **(1 mark)**

(b) Butanedioic acid molecules have two carboxylic acid functional groups, one at each end.

Draw the structure of butanedioic acid. Show all the covalent bonds.

(2 marks)

(c) Propane-1,3-diol and butanedioic acid can act as monomers in a polymerisation reaction.

> This is a different type of polymer to the ones formed by alkene monomers such as ethene and chloroethene.

(i) Name the type of polymer formed when propane-1,3-diol and butanedioic acid react together.

.... **(1 mark)**

(ii) Name the smaller molecule formed when propane-1,3-diol and butanedioic acid react together.

.... **(1 mark)**

2 Polylactic acid, also called PLA, is a biodegradable polyester used to make disposable cups. It forms when many lactic acid molecules react together. The diagram shows the structure of the repeating unit of PLA.

$$\left[\begin{array}{c} \overset{\overset{H}{|}}{\underset{\underset{CH_3}{|}}{C}}-\overset{\overset{O}{||}}{C}-O \end{array}\right]$$

(a) Identify the ester group by drawing a circle around it on the diagram.

.... **(1 mark)**

(b) Suggest a reason that explains why PLA is described as a polyester.

.... **(1 mark)**

> **Guided**

(c) Explain why polyesters are condensation polymers.

A molecule of...

forms each time an .... **(2 marks)**

Biological polymers

1　DNA, proteins and starch are biological polymers. State the type of polymerisation reaction that occurs in the formation of these molecules.

.... **(1 mark)**

2　DNA, deoxyribonucleic acid, is a biological polymer. It is found in the nucleus of cells.

(a)　State the number of **different** monomers found in a DNA molecule.

.... **(1 mark)**

(b)　Give the name of the type of monomers that produce a DNA molecule.

> You are **not** being asked to name each different monomer.

.... **(1 mark)**

3　Proteins are biological polymers. There are many different types of protein in living organisms.

(a)　Give the name of the monomers that produce a protein molecule.

.... **(1 mark)**

(b)　The diagram shows the structure of glycine, an example of the type of monomer that produces proteins.

Glycine contains two different functional groups that allow it to act as a monomer.

Identify these groups by drawing a circle around each one on the diagram. **(2 marks)**

4　Starch is a biological polymer made when glucose monomers react together.

> This is the simplest whole number ratio of the atoms of each element in the compound.

Guided

(a)　The molecular formula of glucose is $C_6H_{12}O_6$.

(i)　Deduce the empirical formula of glucose.

.... **(1 mark)**

(ii)　State why glucose is an example of a **carbohydrate**.

It contains atoms of .... **(1 mark)**

(iii)　Other than a carbohydrate, state the type of substance to which glucose belongs.

> Many of these taste sweet.

.... **(1 mark)**

(b)　Name the larger molecule formed when glucose molecules join together.

.... **(1 mark)**

Polymer problems

1 (a) Explain the meaning of **biodegradable**.

....

.... **(2 marks)**

(b) Landfill sites are used to dispose of many waste materials, including polymers.

    (i) Describe what a landfill site is.

....

.... **(2 marks)**

> **Guided**

    (ii) Explain one problem caused by non-biodegradable polymers in landfill sites.

The polymers do not ....

so the landfill sites .... **(2 marks)**

2 Polymers may be disposed of by incineration (combustion at very high temperatures).

(a) Describe **two** advantages of using incineration rather than landfill sites to dispose of waste polymers.

> What happens to the volume of waste left over after each method of disposal?

   1 ....

   2 .... **(2 marks)**

(b) Explain an environmental problem caused by the incineration of waste polymers.

....

.... **(2 marks)**

3 Different polymers have different properties. Household items may be made from different polymers. For example, bottles often have a clear container with a coloured lid made from a different polymer.

(a) Crude oil is the raw material for making most polymers. Explain an advantage of recycling polymers.

....

.... **(2 marks)**

(b) Give a disadvantage of recycling polymers.   > Look at the information in the stem of the question.

.... **(1 mark)**

4 Microbeads are tiny polymer spheres 5 mm to 10 μm across. They are an ingredient of some cosmetics and toothpastes. These consumer products are usually washed down the drain after use.

(a) Suggest reasons that explain why microbeads pass through waste water treatment plants.

....

.... **(2 marks)**

(b) Explain why microbeads accumulate in living organisms in lakes and seas.

> How could microbeads get into living organisms and why might they not break down?

....

.... **(2 marks)**

Extended response – Hydrocarbons and polymers

Poly(ethene) and a polyester called PET can be made using the appropriate monomers shown in this table.

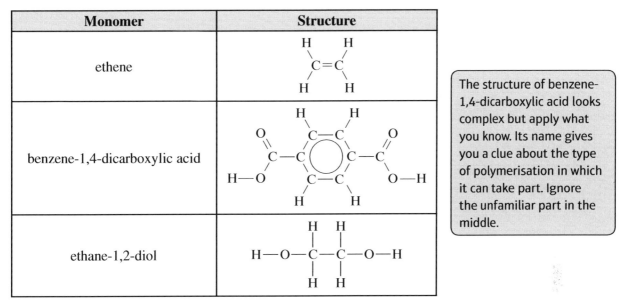

Monomer	Structure
ethene	
benzene-1,4-dicarboxylic acid	
ethane-1,2-diol	

> The structure of benzene-1,4-dicarboxylic acid looks complex but apply what you know. Its name gives you a clue about the type of polymerisation in which it can take part. Ignore the unfamiliar part in the middle.

Explain how the appropriate monomers form poly(ethene) and PET (the polyester). You should include the type of polymerisation that produces each polymer. You could use equations to show the formation of one or both polymers as part of your answer.

....

....

....

....

....

....

....

....

....

....

....

....

....

....

.... **(6 marks)**

Alcohols

1 The table shows some information about three alcohols.

Name of alcohol	Formula	Structure
methanol		H | H—C—O—H | H
ethanol	C_2H_5OH	
		H H H | | | H—C—C—C—O—H | | | H H H

(a) Complete the table. **(4 marks)**

(b) Identify the functional group in alcohols by drawing a circle around it in the bottom diagram. **(1 mark)**

(c) Explain, using information from your completed table, why these three compounds belong to the same homologous series.

....

.... **(2 marks)**

2 Ethanol reacts with sodium to produce hydrogen and a soluble salt called sodium ethoxide:

$$2C_2H_5OH + 2Na \rightarrow H_2 + 2C_2H_5ONa$$

(a) Predict **two** observations that you would see in this reaction.

1 ....

2 .... **(2 marks)**

(b) Ethanol can be oxidised to form ethanoic acid:
$C_2H_5OH + 2[O] \rightarrow CH_3COOH + H_2O$

> [O] in the equation represents oxygen atoms from the oxidising agent used.

Butanol, C_4H_9OH, is a colourless liquid at room temperature.

(i) Predict the products formed by the oxidation of butanol using the same oxidising agent.

.... **(2 marks)**

> Guided

(ii) Write a balanced equation for the oxidation of butanol.

$C_4H_9OH + 2[O] \rightarrow$ .... **(2 marks)**

Making ethanol

1   A student investigates the fermentation of carbohydrates in aqueous solution to produce ethanol. He makes a mixture of sugar, water and yeast. He keeps the mixture at 35°C for a few days in the absence of air.

(a)   Name the products of fermentation.

> There are two products.

.... **(1 mark)**

(b)   Explain why the student added yeast to the mixture.

....

.... **(2 marks)**

(c)   The student repeats the experiment. This time he keeps the mixture at 60°C.

(i)   State how the results would be different from the student's experiment at 35°C.

.... **(1 mark)**

(ii)   Explain why the student's results would be different at 60°C.

....

.... **(2 marks)**

2   Fractional distillation is used to obtain a concentrated solution of ethanol from a fermentation mixture.

(a)   State the physical property that allows ethanol to be separated from water by fractional distillation.

.... **(1 mark)**

Guided

(b)   The diagram shows the apparatus used for fractional distillation.

Describe how this apparatus is used to obtain a concentrated solution of ethanol.

Heat the dilute solution of ethanol using ....

....

....

....

thermometer
water out
fractionating column
condenser
cold water in
dilute solution of ethanol

....

....

....

.... **(4 marks)**

Carboxylic acids

1   Ethanoic acid, CH_3COOH, is a weak acid. Name an indicator that can be used to show that ethanoic acid is acidic, and gives its colour in dilute ethanoic acid.

> Make sure the colour matches the indicator you name.

name of indicator ....

colour in dilute ethanoic acid .... **(2 marks)**

2   Ethanoic acid has the typical properties of an acid.

    (a)   Describe what you would see when a small piece of solid sodium carbonate is added to dilute ethanoic acid in a test tube.

      ....

      .... **(2 marks)**

    (b)   Magnesium ribbon reacts with dilute ethanoic acid. Bubbles of gas are produced.

> This gas is produced when a metal reacts with water or any dilute acid.

      Name the gas produced in the reaction.

      .... **(1 mark)**

3   The diagram shows the structure of ethanoic acid.

    (a)   Identify the functional group in carboxylic acids by drawing a circle around it in the diagram.

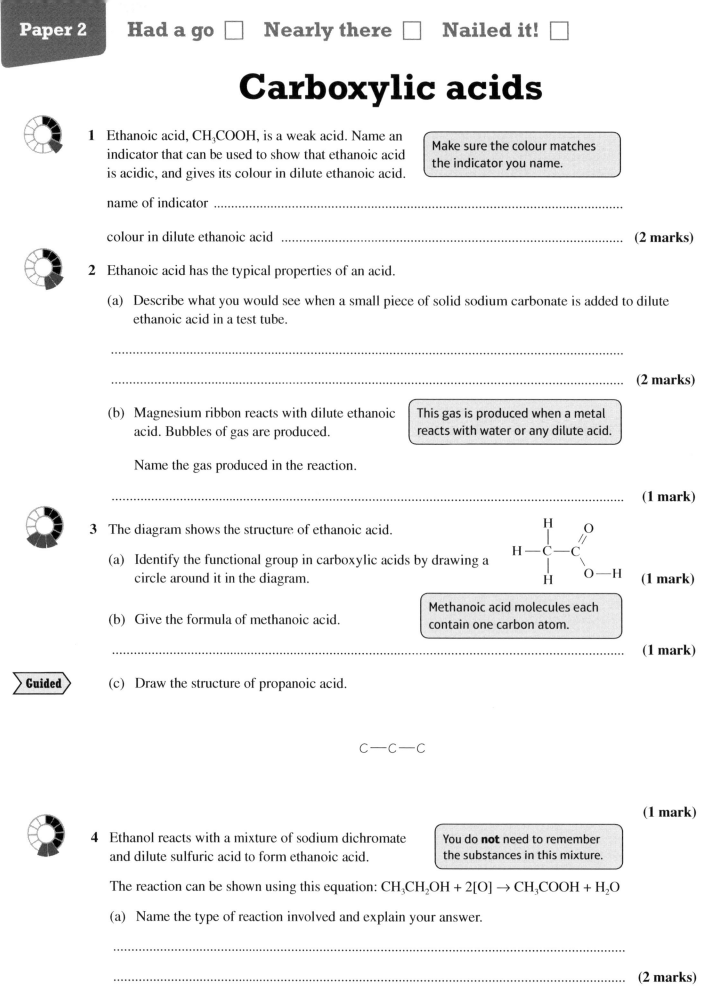

                                                     (1 mark)

    (b)   Give the formula of methanoic acid.

> Methanoic acid molecules each contain one carbon atom.

      .... **(1 mark)**

    Guided   (c)   Draw the structure of propanoic acid.

$$C—C—C$$

                                                     (1 mark)

4   Ethanol reacts with a mixture of sodium dichromate and dilute sulfuric acid to form ethanoic acid.

> You do **not** need to remember the substances in this mixture.

The reaction can be shown using this equation: $CH_3CH_2OH + 2[O] \rightarrow CH_3COOH + H_2O$

    (a)   Name the type of reaction involved and explain your answer.

      ....

      .... **(2 marks)**

    (b)   Name the alcohol needed to produce methanoic acid.

      .... **(1 mark)**

🧪 Practical skills Investigating combustion

1 A student investigates the combustion of some different alcohols. The photo shows the apparatus that she uses.

(a) Explain an improvement that she could make to measure the temperature of the water more safely.

> This could be different apparatus to measure the temperature, or something to help use the thermometer safely.

....

....

.... **(2 marks)**

(b) Suggest reasons that explain why the spirit burner should not be moved while the wick is alight.

....

.... **(2 marks)**

Guided

(c) The bottom of the copper can gradually becomes coated with soot due to incomplete combustion. Explain the effect the formation of soot has on the measured temperature change in the water.

The temperature change will be .... than expected because

....

.... **(2 marks)**

(d) Give two variables that the student should control to make a fair comparison between alcohols.

....

.... **(2 marks)**

2 The table shows the results of an investigation involving two alcohols.

Fuel	Starting temperature of the water (°C)	Final temperature of the water (°C)	Change in temperature of the water (°C)	Mass of fuel burned (g)
ethanol	18	42		0.40
butanol	18	47		0.43

(a) Complete the table to show the changes in the temperature of the water. **(1 mark)**

Guided

(b) Determine which fuel produces the greatest change in temperature per gram of fuel burned.

ethanol: $\left(\dfrac{42 - 18}{0.4}\right) =$ ....

butanol: ....

So .... produces the greatest change per gram of fuel. **(2 marks)**

Nanoparticles

1 Which of the following has approximately the same size as a nanoparticle?

	Object	Approximate size (nm)
☐ A	carbon atom	0.3
☐ B	cold virus	30
☐ C	bacterium	1000
☐ D	red blood cell	8000

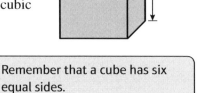

(1 mark)

2 Fool's gold is iron sulfide, FeS_2. It forms gold-coloured cubic crystals.

A fool's gold crystal is found to have sides 10 mm long.

> Remember that a cube has six equal sides.

(a) Calculate the total surface area of this cube.

.... mm² **(2 marks)**

(b) Calculate the volume of this cube.

.... mm³ **(2 marks)**

(c) Calculate the surface area to volume ratio of this cube.

> 🖩 **Maths skills** Divide answer (a) by answer (b). Your answer will have no units because it is a ratio.

.... **(1 mark)**

3 Titanium dioxide is a white solid when in bulk. It absorbs harmful ultraviolet radiation present in sunlight. Nanoparticulate titanium dioxide also absorbs ultraviolet light. Experiments show that titanium dioxide nanoparticles do not easily pass into undamaged skin.

> Solids in bulk are powders and lumps.

(a) Explain the benefits of using a sunscreen containing nanoparticles rather than one containing bulk titanium dioxide.

....

.... **(2 marks)**

(b) Explain a possible risk to sunscreen users associated with titanium dioxide nanoparticles.

....

.... **(2 marks)**

> **Guided**

(c) Titanium dioxide nanoparticles are the catalyst for a self-cleaning coating for window glass. Explain why nanoparticles may be more effective catalysts than the same substances in bulk.

Nanoparticles have a very large ....

so reactant particles .... **(2 marks)**

110

Bulk materials

1 Which of the following rows in the table correctly shows a typical property of each material?

	Glass	Clay ceramics	Polymers	Metals
☐ A	hard	brittle	good conductor of electricity	good conductor of electricity
☐ B	transparent	opaque	poor conductor of heat	brittle
☐ C	poor conductor of heat	poor conductor of electricity	poor conductor of electricity	dull when polished
☐ D	poor conductor of electricity	poor conductor of heat	poor conductor of heat	ductile

(1 mark)

2 The table shows some properties of four metals.

Metal	Melting point (°C)	Density (g/cm³)	Relative electrical conductivity	Relative hardness
chromium	1857	7.2	0.8	8.5
copper	1083	8.9	6.4	3.0
iron	1535	7.9	1.1	4.0
zinc	420	7.1	1.8	2.5

(a) Explain, using information from the table, why copper is used to make electrical cables.

....

.... (2 marks)

(b) Some drill bits can drill through sheets of metal. Friction causes heating during drilling. Explain which metal shown in the table would be the most suitable for making one of these drill bits.

> Your answer should include more than one relevant property from the table.

....

....

.... (3 marks)

3 Car windscreens are made from a composite material. This consists of a thin sheet of tough, transparent polymer glued between two thicker sheets of glass.

Guided ▷ (a) Explain the meaning of the term **composite material**.

Two or more materials combined ....

....

.... (2 marks)

(b) Describe an advantage of using the composite material compared with using glass alone.

....

.... (2 marks)

Extended response – Materials

Car body panels are usually made from steel sheet, pressed into shape. Today, some cars may have body panels made from composite materials. The table shows information about three of these materials.

Material	Cost (£/kg)	Relative strength	Relative stiffness	Brittleness	Notes
FRR	2	0.7	0.6	low	can be coloured / can be pressed into shape
fibreglass	4	0.8	0.4	medium	can be coloured / must be built up in layers
CRP	42	10	10	high	black / must be built up in layers

> The greater the relative strength or stiffness, the stronger or stiffer the material is. A very stiff material is not very flexible.

All three consist of polymer resins reinforced with fibres. FRR contains cotton fibres, fibreglass contains glass fibres and CRP contains carbon fibres.

Evaluate the different composite materials for use in car body panels, such as front wings or doors.

> You need to review the information in the table, and then bring it together to form a conclusion. This will include comparing the strengths and weaknesses of using each material for car body panels.

....

....

....

....

....

....

....

....

....

....

....

....

....

> You should be able to explain why the properties of a material make it suitable for a given use, and to use data to select materials appropriate for specific uses.

....

....

....

.... **(6 marks)**

Timed Test 1

> **Time allowed: 1 hour 45 minutes**
>
> **Total marks: 100**
>
> **Edexcel publishes official Sample Assessment Material on its website. This Timed Test has been written to help you practise what you have learned and may not be representative of a real exam paper.**

1 (a) The table shown in Figure 1 gives the numbers of protons, neutrons and electrons in five different particles (**V, W, X, Y** and **Z**).

Particle	Protons	Neutrons	Electrons
V	8	8	8
W	11	12	11
X	13	14	10
Y	15	16	18
Z	18	22	18

Figure 1

   (i) Which particle is a positively charged **ion**?

     ☐ **A** particle W

     ☐ **B** particle X

     ☐ **C** particle Y

     ☐ **D** particle Z   **(1 mark)**

   (ii) Which particles are **atoms** of non-metals?

     ☐ **A**   particles V and W

     ☐ **B**   particles W and X

     ☐ **C**   particles X and Y

     ☐ **D**   particles V and Z   **(1 mark)**

(b) A sample of neon consists of 90.5% $^{20}_{10}$Ne and 9.5% $^{22}_{10}$Ne.

   (i) Describe, in terms of subatomic particles, why these are isotopes of the same element.   **(4 marks)**

   (ii) Calculate the relative atomic mass, A_r, of neon. Give your answer to one decimal place.   **(3 marks)**

(Total for Question 1 = 9 marks)

2 This question is about elements and the periodic table.

(a) Dmitri Mendeleev (1834–1907) was a Russian chemist who developed a periodic table.

   Give one similarity and one difference between Mendeleev's table and the modern periodic table.   **(2 marks)**

(b) Complete the diagram below to show the electronic configuration of phosphorus, P.

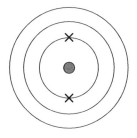

         (1 mark)

(c) Explain, in terms of their electronic configurations, why fluorine and chlorine are placed in group 7.

         (1 mark)

(d) Explain, in terms of their electronic configurations, why magnesium is placed in period 3 but calcium is placed in period 4. **(2 marks)**

(Total for Question 2 = 6 marks)

3 The table shown in Figure 2 gives the formulae of three ions.

Name of ion	Formula of ion
aluminium	Al^{3+}
hydroxide	OH^-
sulfate	SO_4^{2-}

Figure 2

(a) Which of these is the correct formula for aluminium sulfate?

☐ **A** Al_3SO_4

☐ **B** $Al_3(SO_4)_2$

☐ **C** $Al_2(SO_4)_3$

☐ **D** Al_2SO_4 **(1 mark)**

(b) The atomic number of aluminium is 13 and its mass number is 27.

Calculate the numbers of protons, neutrons and electrons in an aluminium **ion**. **(3 marks)**

(c) The melting point of aluminium sulfate is 770°C.

Explain why the melting point of aluminium sulfate is high. **(3 marks)**

(d) Aluminium sulfate is soluble in water. It is used in the treatment of water for drinking.

   (i) A solution of aluminium sulfate is formed by dissolving 35 g of aluminium sulfate in 250 cm³ of water. Calculate the concentration, in g dm⁻³, of this solution. **(2 marks)**

   (ii) A precipitate of aluminium hydroxide is produced during the treatment of water. This sticky solid traps small particles so they sink to the bottom of the water treatment tank.

   Write a balanced ionic equation for the reaction between aluminium ions and hydroxide ions in solution to form aluminium hydroxide. Include state symbols. **(3 marks)**

(Total for Question 3 = 12 marks)

4 Air is a mixture of gases, including nitrogen, oxygen and carbon dioxide.

(a) Why does nitrogen have a low boiling point?

☐ **A** There are weak forces of attraction between nitrogen molecules.

☐ **B** There are weak covalent bonds between nitrogen molecules.

☐ **C** There are weak forces of attraction between nitrogen atoms.

☐ **D** There are weak covalent bonds between nitrogen atoms. **(1 mark)**

(b) Explain how a covalent bond forms. **(2 marks)**

(c) Draw a dot-and-cross diagram to show a molecule of carbon dioxide, CO_2.

Show the outer electrons only. **(2 marks)**

(d) Figure 3 shows the structures of diamond and graphite.

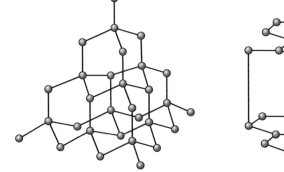
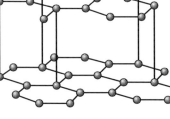

diamond   graphite

Figure 3

Explain, in terms of structure and bonding, why:

(i) diamond has a very high melting point   **(2 marks)**

(ii) graphite is used to make electrodes   **(3 marks)**

(Total for Question 4 = 10 marks)

5 A student adds magnesium to an excess of dilute hydrochloric acid in an evaporating basin. Magnesium chloride solution and hydrogen gas form. When the reaction is complete, the student carefully evaporates the magnesium chloride solution to dryness. The table in Figure 4 shows her results.

Object	Mass (g)
empty evaporating basin	86.43
evaporating basin with magnesium	87.64
magnesium used	
evaporating basin with magnesium chloride	91.22
magnesium chloride formed	

Figure 4

(a) Complete the table to show the mass of magnesium used and the mass of magnesium chloride formed.   **(2 marks)**

(b) Use your answers to part **a** to calculate the mass (g) of chlorine present in the magnesium chloride.   **(1 mark)**

(c) Use your answers to parts **a** and **b** to calculate the **empirical formula** of magnesium chloride.
(A_r of Mg = 24.0 and A_r of Cl = 35.5)   **(3 marks)**

(d) In a separate experiment, a teacher adds 0.45 g of powdered aluminium to excess dilute hydrochloric acid. Aluminium chloride solution and hydrogen form:

$$2Al(s) + 6HCl(aq) \rightarrow 2AlCl_3(aq) + 3H_2(g)$$

(i) Calculate the maximum volume, in dm^3, of hydrogen produced in the reaction.
(1 mol of any gas occupies 24 dm^3 at room temperature and pressure; A_r of Al = 27)   **(3 marks)**

(ii) Describe the chemical test for hydrogen   **(2 marks)**

(Total for Question 5 = 11 marks)

6 This question is about drinking water.

(a) Which of these describes clean drinking water?

☐ **A** a pure substance

☐ **B** a simple molecular compound

☐ **C** a mixture of substances

☐ **D** not potable   **(1 mark)**

(b) Sea water contains 0.469 mol dm^{-3} of sodium chloride, NaCl. Calculate the concentration of sodium chloride in seawater in g dm^{-3}. (A_r of Na = 23.0, A_r of Cl = 35.5)   **(2 marks)**

(c) Drinking water can be made by the simple distillation of seawater.

(i) Describe, in terms of the arrangement and relative energy of water particles, what happens when water boils.   **(2 marks)**

(ii) Suggest a reason that explains why producing large volumes of drinking water by simple distillation is expensive.   **(1 mark)**

(iii) Explain why distilled water, rather than tap water, is suitable for use in chemical analysis.   **(2 marks)**

(d) Fresh water can be made safe for drinking at a water treatment plant. Sedimentation is needed to allow very small particles to settle out. Filtration and chlorination are also needed.

(i) Describe why filtration is needed. **(1 mark)**

(ii) Explain why chlorination is needed. **(2 marks)**

(Total for Question 6 = 11 marks)

7 This question is about making salts.

(a) Which row in the table is correct?

		Soluble in water	Insoluble in water
☐	**A**	silver chloride	lead chloride
☐	**B**	sodium carbonate	calcium sulfate
☐	**C**	sodium chloride	calcium chloride
☐	**D**	barium sulfate	barium nitrate

(1 mark)

(b) Predict whether a precipitate will form when sodium hydroxide solution and iron(III) chloride solution are mixed together. Name any precipitate that forms. **(1 mark)**

(c) Aqueous solutions can be acidic, neutral or alkaline.

(i) State the type of aqueous solution that contains an excess of hydroxide ions, $OH^-(aq)$. **(1 mark)**

(ii) An acidic solution, with a pH of 0.70, contains 0.20 mol dm^{-3} of hydrogen ions, $H^+(aq)$.

Predict the pH of an acidic solution that contains 0.020 mol dm^{-3} of $H^+(aq)$. **(1 mark)**

(iii) Explain, in terms of ions, the difference between a strong acid and a weak acid. **(2 marks)**

(iv) Write a balanced ionic equation for neutralisation. **(1 mark)**

*(d) Plan an experiment to prepare pure, dry crystals of copper chloride, $CuCl_2$, from an insoluble copper compound and a suitable dilute acid. In your answer, include the names of suitable reagents and describe any essential stages. You may wish to write a balanced equation to help with your plan. **(6 marks)**

(Total for Question 7 = 13 marks)

8 This question is about electrolysis and electroplating.

(a) State what is meant by the term **electrolyte**. **(2 marks)**

(b) Copper and chlorine form during the electrolysis of concentrated copper chloride solution.

Which row in the table correctly shows what happens at the negative electrode?

		Product formed	Type of reaction
☐	**A**	copper	reduction
☐	**B**	copper	oxidation
☐	**C**	chlorine	reduction
☐	**D**	chlorine	oxidation

(1 mark)

(c) Aluminium is extracted by the electrolysis of aluminium oxide, dissolved in molten cryolite.

(i) State why aluminium cannot be extracted from aluminium oxide by heating with carbon. **(1 mark)**

(ii) Balance the half equation below for the reaction that occurs at the anode.

..........$O^{2-} \rightarrow O_2 +$ ....e^- **(1 mark)**

(d) Sir Humphry Davy (1778–1829) discovered potassium in 1807 by the electrolysis of molten potassium hydroxide, KOH.

Write a balanced half equation for the reaction that occurs at the cathode. **(2 marks)**

(e) Metal objects can be electroplated with a thin layer of another metal.

    (i) State **two** reasons why this may be done.   **(2 marks)**

    (ii) Steel cutlery can be electroplated with silver.

       Describe the necessary anode, cathode and electrolyte needed to do this.   **(2 marks)**

                                            (Total for Question 8 = 11 marks)

9 This question is about metals.

  (a) Iron is a transition metal. Which of the following is a typical property of transition metals?

        ☐ **A** They form colourless compounds.

        ☐ **B** They have low densities.

        ☐ **C** They rust in air and water.

        ☐ **D** They have high melting points.   **(1 mark)**

  (b) Iron can be extracted by heating iron(III) oxide, Fe_2O_3, with carbon. Iron and carbon dioxide form.

    (i) Write a balanced equation for the reaction.   **(2 marks)**

    (ii) In a blast furnace, the theoretical yield is 2.95×10^5 kg of iron but the actual yield is 2.59×10^5 kg.
Calculate the percentage yield of iron.   **(2 marks)**

  (c) Copper can be extracted by heating copper(I) sulfide in air: $Cu_2S + O_2 \rightarrow 2Cu + SO_2$

    Calculate the atom economy of producing copper in this reaction.

    (A_r of Cu = 63.5, A_r of S = 32.0 and A_r of O = 16.0)   **(3 marks)**

                                          (Total for Question 9 = 8 marks)

10 Ammonia is manufactured from nitrogen and hydrogen by the Haber process:

$$N_2(g) + 3H_2(g) \rightleftharpoons 2NH_3(g) \qquad \text{(forward reaction is exothermic)}$$

  (a) What is the maximum volume of ammonia, NH_3, that could be made from 150 cm³ of hydrogen, H_2?
Assume that the temperature and pressure stay the same.

        ☐ **A** 50 cm³

        ☐ **B** 100 cm³

        ☐ **C** 225 dm³

        ☐ **D** 450 cm³   **(1 mark)**

  (b) Iron is used as a catalyst in the Haber process. Which statement about this is correct?

        ☐ **A** The iron is changed chemically and in mass at the end of the reaction.

        ☐ **B** The time to reach equilibrium is decreased.

        ☐ **C** The equilibrium concentration of ammonia is increased.

        ☐ **D** The equilibrium concentration of ammonia is decreased.   **(1 mark)**

  (c) Give the meaning of the symbol $\rightleftharpoons$ in chemical equations.   **(1 mark)**

*(d) Hydrogen can be manufactured by the reaction of coal with steam in two stages:

    stage 1: $C(s) + H_2O(g) \rightleftharpoons H_2(g) + CO(g)$ (forward reaction is endothermic)

    Carbon monoxide is converted to carbon dioxide by reacting it with more steam:

    stage 2: $CO(g) + H_2O(g) \rightarrow H_2(g) + CO_2(g)$ (exothermic)

    Stage 1 is carried out at a temperature of about 1400°C and a pressure of around 10 atmospheres.

    Stage 2 reduces the concentration of carbon monoxide in the mixture of gases formed in stage 1.

    Explain why these conditions are used in terms of their effect on the rate of reaction, yield of hydrogen and
cost of production.   **(6 marks)**

                                          (Total for Question 10 = 9 marks)

Timed Test 2

Time allowed: 1 hour 45 minutes

Total marks: 100

Edexcel publishes official Sample Assessment Material on its website. This practice exam paper has been written to help you practise what you have learned and may not be representative of a real exam paper.

1   This question is about the alkali metals, the elements in group 1 of the periodic table.

   (a) Which of these shows the typical physical properties of the alkali metals?

     ☐   **A**   soft with relatively low melting points

     ☐   **B**   soft with relatively high melting points

     ☐   **C**   hard with relatively low melting points

     ☐   **D**   hard with relatively high melting points   **(1 mark)**

   (b) Potassium reacts with water. The reaction produces potassium hydroxide solution, KOH, and hydrogen gas, H_2.

     (i)   Write the balanced equation for the reaction between potassium and water. Include state symbols.

                                                                              (3 marks)

     (ii) Describe what is seen when a piece of potassium is added to a trough of water.   **(2 marks)**

   (c) The electronic configuration of lithium is 2.1.

     (i)   Write the electronic configurations of sodium and potassium.   **(2 marks)**

     (ii) Explain the trend in the reactivity of the group 1 metals.   **(3 marks)**

                                                (Total for Question 1 = 11 marks)

2   This question is about the halogens, the elements in group 7 of the periodic table.

   (a) Which row in the table correctly shows the colours and physical states of the halogens at room temperature and pressure?

		Chlorine	Bromine	Iodine
☐	**A**	pale yellow liquid	red-brown liquid	red-brown solid
☐	**B**	yellow-green gas	dark grey liquid	dark grey solid
☐	**C**	yellow-green gas	red-brown liquid	dark grey solid
☐	**D**	yellow-green gas	purple liquid	red-brown liquid

                                                           (1 mark)

   (b) Describe the chemical test for chlorine.   **(2 marks)**

 *(c) In aqueous solution, chlorine reacts with sodium iodide, NaI. Sodium chloride solution and iodine solution form:

     $Cl_2 + 2NaI \rightarrow 2NaCl + I_2$

     Explain, in terms of electron gain and loss, why this reaction is a redox reaction. You may include half equations in your answer.   **(6 marks)**

                                                (Total for Question 2 = 9 marks)

3   A student investigates the rate of reaction between calcium carbonate (marble chips) and excess dilute hydrochloric acid: $CaCO_3(s) + 2HCl(aq) \rightarrow CaCl_2(aq) + H_2O(l) + CO_2(g)$

   (a) Which of these would increase the rate of the reaction?

     ☐   **A**   adding water to the acid

     ☐   **B**   increasing the volume of acid

     ☐   **C**   increasing the size of the marble chips

     ☐   **D**   using calcium carbonate powder instead of marble chips   **(1 mark)**

(b) The student added 0.50 g of calcium carbonate to 50 cm³ of 0.40 mol dm⁻³ hydrochloric acid. Show, by calculation, that the acid is in excess. (M_r of $CaCO_3$ = 100) **(4 marks)**

(c) The student measured the volume of carbon dioxide produced until all the calcium carbonate had reacted. Figure 1 shows the results that she obtained at 20° C.

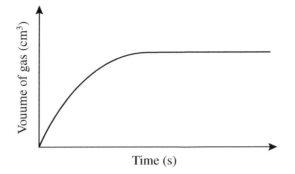

Figure 1

(i) Sketch, on the same axes above, the results that the student would obtain by repeating the experiment at a higher temperature. **(2 marks)**

(ii) Explain, in terms of particles, why increasing the temperature has this effect on the rate of reaction. **(3 marks)**

(Total for Question 3 = 10 marks)

4 Hydrogen peroxide decomposes to form water and oxygen: $2H_2O_2(aq) \rightarrow 2H_2O(l) + O_2(g)$

The reaction is exothermic.

(a) Draw and label the reaction profile diagram for this reaction, clearly labelling the activation energy.

(3 marks)

(b) Manganese dioxide, MnO_2, acts as a catalyst for this reaction.

(i) On the same axes above, draw the reaction profile for the same reaction in the presence of a catalyst. Label this reaction profile with an **X**. **(1 mark)**

(ii) Describe what is meant by the term **catalyst**. **(3 marks)**

(iii) Explain, in terms of energy, how a catalyst works. **(2 marks)**

(c) If a piece of raw liver is added to hydrogen peroxide solution, rapid bubbling is observed.

Suggest reasons that explain this observation. **(2 marks)**

(Total for Question 4 = 11 marks)

5 Ethene undergoes complete combustion in oxygen to form carbon dioxide and water:

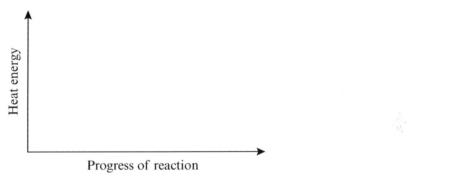

(a) Calculate, using the bond energies shown in Figure 2, the energy change for this reaction.

Bond	Bond energy (kJ mol^{-1})
C–H	413
O=O	498
C=O	805
C=C	612
O–H	464

Figure 2

(4 marks)

(b) Explain, in terms of the energy involved in breaking bonds and making bonds, why this reaction is exothermic. **(2 marks)**

(c) Ethene is a member of the alkene homologous series. State **two** features of an homologous series.   **(2 marks)**

(Total for Question 5 = 8 marks)

6 This question is about crude oil.

(a) Which of these statements about crude oil is correct?

☐ **A** It is a renewable resource.

☐ **B** It contains molecules with carbon atoms in rings and chains.

☐ **C** It is a complex mixture of carbohydrates.

☐ **D** At room temperature, it contains only liquids.   **(1 mark)**

(b) Crude oil is separated in fractions using fractional distillation. Figure 3 shows an oil fractional distillation column and the main fractions obtained from it.

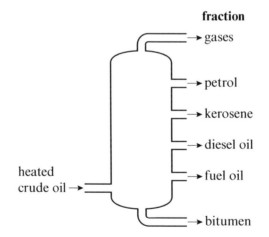

Figure 3

Identify the fraction that:

(i) has the highest boiling point   **(1 mark)**

(ii) is used as a fuel for large ships and some power stations.   **(1 mark)**

(c) State why crude oil may be described as a finite resource.   **(1 mark)**

(d) Explain how the different substances in crude oil are separated by fractional distillation.   **(4 marks)**

(Total for Question 6 = 8 marks)

7 This question is about the Earth's atmosphere.

(a) Which of these gases was the most abundant in the Earth's earliest atmosphere?

☐ **A** nitrogen

☐ **B** oxygen

☐ **C** argon

☐ **D** carbon dioxide   **(1 mark)**

(b) Explain how the amount of carbon dioxide in the atmosphere changed over millions of years.   **(3 marks)**

(c) The combustion of fossil fuels needs oxygen, found in air.

    (i) Describe the chemical test for oxygen.   **(2 marks)**

    (ii) The combustion of fossil fuels releases carbon dioxide into the air. Explain how this gas could cause a change in the temperature of the Earth.   **(3 marks)**

(d) The combustion of some fossil fuels releases sulfur dioxide into the air. Explain **two** problems caused when this gas dissolves in rainwater.   **(3 marks)**

(Total for Question 7 = 12 marks)

8 Three metal compounds (**A**, **B** and **C**) are tested separately using:

- flame tests
- silver nitrate solution acidified with dilute nitric acid
- dilute sodium hydroxide solution
- barium chloride solution acidified with dilute hydrochloric acid.

The table (Figure 4) shows the results of all these tests.

Metal compound	Flame test	Silver nitrate solution	Sodium hydroxide solution	Barium chloride solution
A	orange-red	white precipitate	white precipitate	no visible change
B	blue-green	yellow precipitate	blue precipitate	no visible change
C	no colour change	no visible change	green precipitate	white precipitate

Figure 4

(a) Deduce the names of compounds **A** and **B**.   **(4 marks)**

(b) (i) Identify the cation present in compound **C**.   **(1 mark)**

    (ii) On standing in air, the green precipitate formed when dilute sodium hydroxide solution is added to compound **C** gradually becomes an orange-brown precipitate. When the mixture is warmed, ammonia gas is given off. Suggest reasons that explain these observations.   **(3 marks)**

    (iii) Identify the anion present in compound **C**, as shown by the results in Figure 4.   **(1 mark)**

    (iv) Each unit of compound **C** contains three cations and two anions. Deduce the formula of compound **C**.   **(2 marks)**

(Total for Question 8 = 11 marks)

9   The molecules contained in a substance can be modelled in different ways. Figure 5 shows some information taken from a chemistry textbook.

Chemical formulae for ethene

Molecular formula	Empirical formula	Structural formula	Displayed formula
C_2H_4	CH_2	$CH_2{=}CH_2$	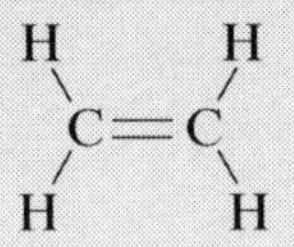 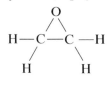

Figure 5

   (a) Give the molecular formula of propane.   **(1 mark)**

   (b) Give the empirical formula of ethane.   **(1 mark)**

   (c) Give the structural formula of propene.   **(1 mark)**

   (d) Draw the displayed formula of but-2-ene, showing all the covalent bonds.   **(2 marks)**

   (e) Ethene reacts with bromine, Br_2. A single product forms in the reaction.

   (i) Write an equation for this reaction. Use structural formulae for the substances that contain carbon.   **(1 mark)**

   (ii) Name the type of reaction involved.   **(1 mark)**

   (f) Explain how bromine water may be used to distinguish between ethane and ethene.   **(2 marks)**

   (Total for Question 9 = 9 marks)

10 Figure 6 shows the displayed formula of epoxyethane, C_2H_4O.

$$\begin{array}{c} O \\ / \backslash \\ H-C-C-H \\ / \quad\quad \backslash \\ H \quad\quad\quad H \end{array}$$

Figure 6

Epoxyethane is an important feedstock for the manufacture of detergents and condensation polymers. It is manufactured by the reaction between ethene and oxygen. A silver catalyst ensures that epoxyethane is produced, rather than carbon dioxide and water.

Scientists have discovered that silver nanoparticles catalyse the direct production of epoxyethane from ethanol. This may lead to a sustainable way to manufacture epoxyethane.

   (a) Draw the displayed formula of ethanol, showing all the covalent bonds.   **(1 mark)**

   *(b) Describe how a concentrated solution of ethanol may be produced, starting with sugars from plants.   **(6 marks)**

   (c) Suggest reasons that explain why the manufacture of epoxyethane from ethanol may be more sustainable than its manufacture from ethene.   **(2 marks)**

   (d) Describe the properties of silver nanoparticles that allow them to act as a catalyst.   **(2 marks)**

   (Total for Question 10 = 11 marks)

Answers

1. Formulae

1 answer C (1)

2 An element is a substance made from atoms (1) with the same number of protons (1).

3 (a) Compounds contain two or more different elements chemically joined together (1), but Cl_2 shows that chlorine contains only (two atoms of) one element (1).

   (b) Cl_2 shows that chlorine exists as two chlorine atoms joined together (1), and chlorine is a non-metal (and nearly all non-metal elements are molecular) (1).

4 1 mark for each correct formula: water, H_2O; carbon dioxide, CO_2; methane, CH_4; sulfuric acid, H_2SO_4; sodium, Na

5 (a) 3 (1)   (b) 7 (1)

6 It contains one carbon atom and three oxygen atoms (1); it has two negative charges overall (1).

2. Equations

1 answer B (1)

2 (a) sodium hydroxide + hydrochloric acid → sodium chloride + water (1)

   (b) $NaOH + HCl \rightarrow NaCl + H_2O$ (1)

3 (a) 1 mark for all four state symbols in the correct order: (s), (l), (aq), (g)

   (b) There are the same numbers of atoms (1) of each element on both sides of the equation (1).

4 (a) $2Cu + O_2 \rightarrow 2CuO$ (1)

   (b) $2Al + Fe_2O_3 \rightarrow Al_2O_3 + 2Fe$ (1)

   (c) $Mg + 2HNO_3 \rightarrow Mg(NO_3)_2 + H_2$ (1)

   (d) $Na_2CO_3 + 2HCl \rightarrow 2NaCl + H_2O + CO_2$ (1)

   (e) $4Fe + 3O_2 \rightarrow 2Fe_2O_3$ or $Fe + 1\frac{1}{2}O_2 \rightarrow Fe_2O_3$ (1)

   (f) $Cl_2 + 2NaBr \rightarrow 2NaCl + Br_2$ (1)

3. Ionic equations

1 An ion is a charged particle (1) formed when an atom or group of atoms loses or gains electrons (1).

2 (a) silver ion Ag^+; (1) iodide ion I^- (1)

   (b) $Ag^+(aq) + I^-(aq) \rightarrow AgI(s)$
   1 mark for balanced equation, 1 mark for state symbols

3 (a) hydrogen ion H^+ (1); carbonate ion CO_3^{2-} (1)

   (b) $2H^+ + CO_3^{2-} \rightarrow H_2O + CO_2$
   1 mark for formulae, 1 mark for balancing

4 (a) $Fe^{2+} + 2OH^- \rightarrow Fe(OH)_2$ (1)

   (b) $Fe^{3+} + 3OH^- \rightarrow Fe(OH)_3$ (1)

5 (a) $H^+ + OH^- \rightarrow H_2O$ (1)

   (b) water (1)

6 (a) K^+ (1), Br^- (1), Cl^- (1)

   (b) $Cl_2 + 2Br^- \rightarrow 2Cl^- + Br_2$

1 mark for Cl_2 and Br_2, 1 mark for balancing

4. Hazards, risk and precautions

1 A hazard is something that could cause damage to/harm someone/something (1) or cause adverse health effects (1).

2 the chance that someone or something will be harmed (1), if exposed to a hazard (1)

3 to indicate the dangers associated with the contents (1); to inform people about safe-working precautions with these substances (1)

4 1 mark for each correct new line (if more than four new lines drawn, subtract 1 mark for each extra line):

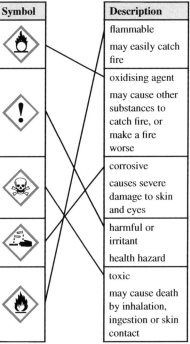

Symbol	Description
	flammable
	may easily catch fire
	oxidising agent
	may cause other substances to catch fire, or make a fire worse
	corrosive
	causes severe damage to skin and eyes
	harmful or irritant
	health hazard
	toxic
	may cause death by inhalation, ingestion or skin contact

5 precaution for 1 mark with appropriate reason for 1 mark, e.g. wear gloves to avoid skin contact because concentrated nitric acid is corrosive/nitrogen dioxide is toxic; work in a fume cupboard to avoid breathing in nitrogen dioxide (which is toxic)

5. Atomic structure

1 answer A (1)

2 2 or 3 correct (1), 4 or 5 correct (2), 6 correct (3)

Particle	proton	neutron	electron
Relative mass	1		1/1836
Relative charge	+1	0	
Position		nucleus	shell

3 The atom contains equal numbers of protons and electrons/1 proton and 1 electron (1); protons and electrons have equal but opposite charges/relative charge of proton is +1 and relative charge of electron is −1 (1).

4 These particles were not discovered until later. (1)

5 $(2.70 \times 10^{-10} \text{ m})/(1.03 \times 10^{-14} \text{ m}) = 26\,200$

1 mark for working out, 1 mark for correct answer to 3 significant figures

6 (a) Most of an atom is empty space. (1)

   (b) The nucleus is positively charged (1) because like charges repel (1).

   (c) Only a few particles come close to the nucleus (1) because it is very small compared with the rest of the atom (1).

6. Isotopes

1 The mass number of an atom is the total number of protons and neutrons (in the nucleus). (1)

2 answer A (1)

3 a substance whose atoms all have the same number of protons (1) which is unique to that element/different from all other elements (1)

4 (a) 1 mark for each correct row:

Isotope	Protons	Neutrons	Electrons
hydrogen-1	1	0	1
hydrogen-2	1	1	1
hydrogen-3	1	2	1

   (b) Their nuclei have the same number of protons (1) but different numbers of neutrons (1).

5 Some elements have different isotopes (1) so their relative atomic masses are a (weighted) mean value (1).

6 Relative abundance of neon-22 = 9.5% (1)

Mass of 100 atoms = $(20 \times 90.5) + (22 \times 9.5)$
= 2019 (1)

$A_r = 2019/100 = 20.19$
= 20.2 (to one decimal place) (1)

7. Mendeleev's table

1 (a) answer D (1)

   (b) the properties of the elements and their compounds (1)

2 (a) two similarities for 1 mark each, e.g. elements put into groups; elements put into periods; elements with similar properties put into the same groups

   (b) three differences for 1 mark each, e.g. Mendeleev's table had gaps/fewer elements/did not include the noble gases/ was arranged in order of increasing relative atomic mass (not atomic number);

did not have a block of transition metals; had two elements in some spaces

3 (a) The relative atomic mass of tellurium is greater than that of iodine (1) and Mendeleev thought that he had arranged the elements in order of increasing relative atomic mass (1).

(b) Atoms of tellurium have fewer protons/ lower atomic number than iodine/tellurium has some isotopes with higher masses than iodine (1); elements are arranged in order of increasing atomic number in the modern periodic table (1).

4 He predicted properties of undiscovered elements. (1)

8. The periodic table

1 answer B (1)

2 (a) **A** and **B** (1)
(b) **A, B, C, D** (all four for 1 mark)
(c) **B** and **E** (1)

3 (a) the position of an element (1) on the periodic table (1)
(b) the number of protons (1) in the nucleus of an atom (1)
(c) discovery of protons/discovery of atomic structure/better technology available to study atoms (1)

4 Each element has a unique atomic number/ unique number of protons/unique space on the periodic table (1); there are only six spaces (between sodium and argon) so there can be only six elements (1).

9. Electronic configurations

1 (a) 2.1 (1)
(b) There are three electrons, so there must be three protons (1), so the four shaded circles must be neutrons (1).
(c) two shells (1); two electrons in first shell, six in the second (1), e.g.

2 (a) Both have 7 electrons (1) in their outer shell (1).
(b) Number of occupied shells is the same as the period number (1); fluorine has two occupied shells and chlorine has three (1).

3 (a) 2.8.8.2 (1)
(b) 2.8.5 (1)

4 group 0/8/18 (1) because it has a full outer shell (1)

10. Ions

1 answer D (1)

2 (a) 10 (1)
(b) 2.8 (1)

3 1 mark for each correct row:

Ion	Atomic number	Mass number	Protons	Neutrons	Electrons
N^{3-}	7	15	7	8	10
K^+	19	40	19	21	18
Ca^{2+}	20	40	20	20	18
S^{2-}	16	32	16	16	18
Br^-	35	81	35	46	36

4 three shells and 2.8.7 electrons in the chlorine atom (1); three shells and 2.8.8 electrons in the chloride ion (1); brackets with negative sign (1), e.g.

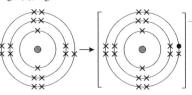

11. Formulae of ionic compounds

1 answer D (1)

2 1 mark for each correct formula:

	Cl^-	S^{2-}	OH^-
K^+	KCl	K_2S	KOH
Ca^{2+}	$CaCl_2$	CaS	$Ca(OH)_2$
Fe^{3+}	$FeCl_3$	Fe_2S_3	$Fe(OH)_3$
NH_4^+	NH_4Cl	$(NH_4)_2S$	NH_4OH

	NO_3^-	SO_4^{2-}	
K^+	KNO_3	K_2SO_4	
Ca^{2+}	$Ca(NO_3)_2$	$CaSO_4$	
Fe^{3+}	$Fe(NO_3)_3$	$Fe_2(SO_4)_3$	
NH_4^+	NH_4NO_3	$(NH_4)_2SO_4$	

3 (a) $2Mg + O_2 \rightarrow 2MgO$ (1 mark for correct formulae, 1 mark for balancing)
(b) (i) The nitrogen atom has five electrons in its outer shell (1); it gains three electrons to complete its outer shell/ form an ion (1).
(ii) Mg_3N_2 (1)
(iii) Nitride ion contains only nitrogen (1) but nitrate ion also contains oxygen (1).

4 1 mark for each correct name:

	S^{2-}	SO_4^{2-}	Cl^-	ClO_3^-
Name	sulfide	sulfate	chloride	chlorate

12. Properties of ionic compounds

1 answer A (1)

2 (a) + and – signs drawn as shown (1)

(b) strong electrostatic forces (1) between oppositely charged ions (1)

3 (a) strong (electrostatic) forces of attraction/ ionic bonds between **ions** (1) which need a lot of heat/energy to break/overcome (1)
(b) MgO has stronger (ionic) bonds than NaCl (1)

4 (a) When calcium chloride is a liquid, its ions are free to move (1) and ions are charged particles (1).
(b) Its **ions** are not free to move/are held in fixed positions/a lattice. (1)
(c) Dissolve it in water. (1)

13. Covalent bonds

1 answer B (1)

2 when a **pair** of electrons (1) is **shared** between two atoms (1)

3 (a) A fluorine atom has one unpaired electron in its outer shell (1) so it shares this electron with another fluorine atom (1).
(b) There is one covalent bond (1) between two hydrogen atoms in a molecule (1).
(c) (i) correct diagram, e.g.

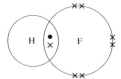

one pair of dots and crosses in shared area (1); three pairs of dots and three pairs of crosses (1)

(ii) correct diagram, e.g.

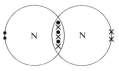

one pair of dots and crosses in shared area (1); (three) pairs of dots/crosses on F only (1)

4 (a) correct diagram, e.g.

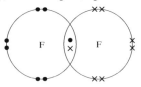

three pairs of dots and crosses in shared area (1); one pair of dots and one pair of crosses (1)
(b) N≡N (1)

14. Simple molecular substances

1 answer C (1)

2 substance B because: it has a low melting point/lowest melting point (1); it is (almost) insoluble in water (1); and it does not conduct electricity when solid or liquid (1)

3 (a) Sulfur hexafluoride molecules are not charged (1) and have no electrons that are free to move (1).
(b) The intermolecular forces between water and sulfur hexafluoride molecules (1) are weaker than those between water molecules (1) and those between sulfur hexafluoride molecules (1).

4 As the relative formula mass increases so does the boiling point (1) because the intermolecular forces become stronger/there are more intermolecular forces to overcome (1).

15. Giant molecular substances

1 answer B (1)

2 (a) carbon (1)
(b) four (1)
(c) giant molecular/giant covalent (1)

3 (a) Each carbon atom forms four covalent bonds (1); in a regular lattice structure (1); the bonds are strong/it is difficult to separate atoms from the structure (1).
(b) The layers in graphite can slide over each other (1) because there are weak forces between the layers (1).
(c) Each carbon atom only forms three bonds (1) so there are (outer) electrons that are delocalised/free to move (1).

16. Other large molecules

1. answer C (1)
2. (a) carbon (1)
   (b) covalent (1)
3. (a) Graphene has covalent (1) bonds in a giant/lattice structure (1) and these bonds are strong (1).
   (b) Each carbon atom only forms three bonds (1) so there are (outer) electrons that are delocalised/free to move (1).
4. It has a simple molecular structure (1) with intermolecular forces (1) that are weak/easily overcome (1).

17. Metals

1. 1 mark for each correct tick (deduct 1 mark for each tick over four ticks)

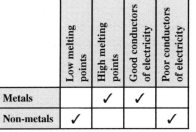

	Low melting points	High melting points	Good conductors of electricity	Poor conductors of electricity
Metals		✓	✓	
Non-metals	✓			✓

2. having a high mass (1) for its volume/size (1) **or** small volume (1) for its mass (1)
3. (a) +/2+ inside the circles (1); delocalised electrons/sea of electrons (1)
   (b) Layers of atoms/(positive) ions (1) can slide over each other (1).
   (c) Delocalised electrons (1) can move through the structure (1).
4. Metallic bonds require a lot of energy to break (1) because there are strong electrostatic forces of attraction (1) between positive metal ions and delocalised electrons (1).
5. Calcium reacts with water (1) to form a soluble product/soluble calcium hydroxide (1).

18. Limitations of models

1. answer B (1)
2. (a) A, B, C (1) (d) B (1)
   (b) A, B (1) (e) C, D (1)
   (c) C, D (1)
3. Answer must include at least one advantage and one disadvantage to gain full marks. (3)

   Advantages of ball and stick include, for 1 mark each: shape of molecule shown; can be modelled in three dimensions (e.g. using a modelling kit).

   Disadvantages of ball and stick include, for 1 mark each: element symbols not shown; bonding electrons not shown; non-bonding electrons not shown.

19. Relative formula mass

1. (a) 18 (1)   2 (a) 74 (1)
   (b) 64 (1)   (b) 78 (1)
   (c) 102 (1)   (c) 164 (1)
   (d) 53.5 (1)   (d) 132 (1)
   (e) 111 (1)   (e) 342 (1)
   (f) 133.5 (1)

20. Empirical formulae

1. (a) to make sure the reaction had finished/all the magnesium had reacted (1)
   (b) use tongs/allow the crucible to cool down (1) to prevent skin burns (1)
   (c) mass of oxygen reacted = 0.16 g (1)

Mg	O
0.25/24 = 0.0104	0.16/16 = 0.010 (1)
0.0104/0.010 = 1.04	0.010/0.010 = 1.00 (1)

Empirical formula is MgO (1)

2. correct answer without working for one mark only, otherwise:

Fe	Cl
11.2/56 = 0.20	21.3/35.5 = 0.60 (1)
0.20/0.20 = 1.0	0.60/0.20 = 3.0 (1)

Empirical formula is $FeCl_3$ (1)

3. M_r of NO_2 = 46 (1)

   Ratio is 92/46 = 2, so molecular formula is N_2O_4 (1)

21. Conservation of mass

1. (a) It is a closed system because no substances can enter or leave (1).
   (b) The total mass will stay the same (1) because mass is conserved in chemical reactions (1).
2. 35.1 g (1) **First mark is for the working out, shown in the Guided example.**
3. M_r of O_2 = 32 and M_r of MgO = 40 (1)

   (1×32) = 32 g of O_2 makes (2×40) = 80 g of MgO (1)

   12.6 g of O_2 makes $80 \times (12.6/32)$ = 31.5 g of MgO (1)
4. M_r of $CaCO_3$ = 100 and M_r of CaO = 56 (1)

   (1×100) = 100 kg of $CaCO_3$ makes (1×56) = 56 kg of CaO (1)

   12.5 kg of $CaCO_3$ makes $56 \times (12.5/100)$ = 7.00 kg of CaO (1)

22. Reacting mass calculations

1. answer D (1)
2. (a) The mass of copper oxide formed increases as the mass of copper carbonate increases. (1)
   but
   The mass of copper oxide formed is **directly** proportional to the mass of copper carbonate (2).
   (b) Copper carbonate is the limiting reagent/only reagent (1) so atoms can come only from copper carbonate (1).
3. mass of chlorine reacted = 32.5 g − 11.2 g
   = 21.3 g (1)

   all three amounts for 1 mark:

   amount of iron = 11.2/56 = 0.2 mol

   amount of chlorine = 21.3/71 = 0.3 mol

   amount of iron(III) chloride = 32.5/162.5 = 0.2 mol

   ratio of $Fe:Cl_2:FeCl_3$ = 0.2:0.3:0.2 (1)

   whole number ratio of $Fe:Cl_2:FeCl_3$ = 2:3:2

   so equation must be:
   $2Fe + 3Cl_2 \rightarrow 2FeCl_3$ (1)

23. Concentration of solution

1. (a) 2 dm^3 (1)
   (b) 0.5 dm^3 (1)
   (c) 0.025 dm^3 (1)
2. concentration = (10/250) × 1000
   = 40 g dm^{-3} (1)
3. (a) 50 g dm^{-3} (1)
   (b) 36.5 g dm^{-3} (1)
   (c) 10 g dm^{-3} (1)
4. (a) mixture of a solute and water/solution in which the solvent is water (1)
   (b) 100 g (1)
   (c) mass of NaOH in
   50 cm^3 = 40 × 50/1000 = 2 g (1)

   new concentration = (mass/250) × 1000
   = (2/250) × 1000 = 8 g dm^{-3} (1)

24. Avogadro's constant and moles

1. Avogadro's number/Avogadro's constant (1)
2. (a) 65.5 g (1)   4 (a) 3.0 mol (1)
   (b) 48 g (1)   (b) 4.0 mol (1)
   (c) 5.4 g (1)   (c) 0.600 mol (1)
3. (a) 0.5 mol (1)   5 1.35×10^{24} (1)
   (b) 2.5 mol (1)   6 15 mol (1)
   (c) 0.25 mol (1)

25. Extended response – Types of substance

*Answer could include the following points.

graphite uses and properties:
- lubricant because it is soft/the softest in the table/10 times softer than copper
- electrodes because it is a good conductor of electricity/conductivity is 100 times less than copper/100 million times better than diamond

graphite bonding and structure:
- giant covalent/giant molecular structure
- strong covalent bonds
- each carbon atom is bonded to three other carbon atoms
- layers of carbon atoms
- weak forces between layers
- layers can slide past each other (making it slippery so that it can be used as a lubricant)
- one free electron per carbon atom
- delocalised electrons
- electrons can move through the structure (allowing it to conduct electricity for use as an electrode)

diamond uses and properties:
- cutting tools because it is very hard/100 times harder than copper/1000 times harder than graphite

diamond bonding and structure:
- giant covalent/giant molecular structure
- strong covalent bonds
- each carbon atom is bonded to four other carbon atoms
- three-dimensional lattice structure
- a lot of energy is needed to break the many strong bonds
- rigid structure

26. States of matter

1. answer C (1)
2. (a) freezing/solidifying (1)
   (b) condensing (1)
3. The chemical composition is unchanged. (1)

4 (a) solid: close together and regular pattern (1); vibrate about fixed positions (1)

   liquid: close together and random (1); move around each other/slide about in groups (1)

   gas: far apart and random (1); move quickly in all directions (1)

   (b) gas (1) because the particles are moving freely/moving fastest/have the most kinetic energy (1)

5 The arrangement changes from random to regular (1) and the movement changes from moving around each other (in groups) to vibrating about fixed positions (1).

6 liquid (1)

27. Pure substances and mixtures

1 (a) The atoms of an element all have the same atomic number/number of protons (1) but atoms of Na and Cl_2 have different atomic numbers/numbers of protons (1).

   (b) substance containing two or more elements (1) **chemically** combined/joined together (1)

2 (a) **B** 0.24 and **C** 0.03 (1)

   (b) None of the samples is pure (1); all contain some residue/dissolved solid/solid mixed in (1).

3 Pure substances (e.g. tin and silver) have a sharp melting point (1) but mixtures (e.g. solder) melt over a range of temperatures (1).

4 (a) The salts increase the boiling point. (1)

   (b) The boiling point will increase further (1) because the concentration of dissolved salt will increase (1) as the water leaves the seawater (1).

28. Distillation

1 answer C (1)

2 (a) The vapour is cooled (1) and condensed/turned from gas to liquid (1).

   (b) The temperature of the water increases (1) because it is heated up by the vapour/energy is transferred from the vapour to the water by heating (1).

3 (a) They have different boiling points. (1)

   (b) Ethanol because it has a lower boiling point than water (1); it boils/evaporates first (1).

   (c) one of the following for 1 mark:
   - more energy is transferred by heating
   - hot vapour and cold water flow in opposite directions
   - the condenser will be full of cold water/will not contain any air

29. Filtration and crystallisation

1 second box ticked (1); fourth box ticked (1) **Deduct one mark for each extra tick above two ticks.**

2 (a) $2KI(aq) + Pb(NO_3)_2(aq) \rightarrow 2KNO_3(aq) + PbI_2(s)$

   1 mark for correct balancing; 1 mark for correct state symbols

   (b) (i) Its particles are too large to pass through. (1)

      (ii) to remove excess potassium iodide solution/lead nitrate solution/potassium nitrate solution (1)

3 (a) filtration/filtering (1)

   (b) (i) **water** evaporates (1); solution becomes saturated (1); crystals form as more **water** evaporates (1)

      (ii) to dry the crystals (1)

   (c) two from the following, for one mark each: heat the solution slowly; do not evaporate all of the water; leave to cool down so crystals form

30. Paper chromatography

1 (a) Pencil does not dissolve in the solvent. (1)

   (b) mixture because it contains more than one substance/four substances (1); pure substances only contain one substance (1)

   (c) **A** and **B** (1)

   (d) The orange squash does contain X because it contains spots with the same R_f values/which move the same distances as the two spots in X (1).

   (e) It is insoluble in the solvent/mobile phase/has very strong bonds with the stationary phase/has very weak bonds with the mobile phase. (1)

2 correctly measured distance from start line to spot 28 mm (1)

   correctly measured distance from start line to solvent front 35 mm (1)

   $R_f = 0.8$ (no units) (1)

31. Investigating inks

1 (a) distance travelled by the spot/dye (1); distance travelled by the solvent/solvent front (1)

   (b) The measurements will be more precise/have a higher resolution (1) so the R_f value will be more accurate/closer to the true value (1).

2 (a) to stop the solution boiling over (into the condenser) (1) so that the solvent collected is not contaminated with the solution/so that the vapour is not produced faster than it can be condensed (1)

   (b) The apparatus will get very hot/solvent vapour (e.g. steam) will escape. (1)

3 (a) (highly) flammable (1)

   (b) two from the following for 1 mark each (precaution and reason needed for each mark):
   - avoid naked flames because the liquid is flammable
   - wear gloves because it can cause skin dryness
   - work in a fume cupboard/keep lab well ventilated because vapour causes dizziness

32. Drinking water

1 answer A (1)

2 (a) to sterilise the water/to kill microbes (1)

   (b) The concentration of chlorine is very low (1); low enough to kill microbes without being harmful to people (1).

3 sedimentation (1) to remove large insoluble particles (1)

   filtration (1) to remove small insoluble particles (1)

4 Unlike tap water, distilled water does not contain dissolved salts. (1). These would interfere with the analysis/react with test substances/give a false-positive result. (1)

5 (a) **simple** distillation (1)

   (b) a lot of energy is needed/a lot of fuel is needed (1)

6 $Al_2(SO_4)_3(aq) + 6H_2O(l) \rightarrow 2Al(OH)_3(s) + 3H_2SO_4(aq)$ (1)

33. Extended response – Separating mixtures

*Answer could include the following points.

physical states:
- substance A is solid; substances B and C are liquids

separating A from B and C:
- substance A is insoluble in B and C
- so it cannot be separated by paper chromatography
- but it can be separated from B and C by filtration
- substance A collects as a residue in the filter paper
- it can be washed with B or C on the filter paper
- then dried in a warm oven
- below 115 °C to stop it melting

separating B and C:
- (after filtration) the filtrate is a mixture of substances B and C
- they have different boiling points
- so they can be separated by **fractional** distillation
- substance B has the lower boiling point
- substance B distils off first (and can be collected)
- continue heating to leave substance C in the flask

34. Acids and alkalis

1 (a) The green colour means that the indicator is neutral (1); neutral pH is 7 (1).

   (b) red/orange (1)

   (c) hydrogen ion (1)

2 (a) $2Mg + O_2 \rightarrow 2MgO$

      1 mark for correct formulae, 1 mark for correct balancing

   (b) It is alkaline/contains an alkali/has a pH greater than 7. (1)

3 $NaOH(aq) \rightarrow Na^+(aq) + OH^-(aq)$ (1)

4 methyl orange: yellow, red; (1) phenolphthalein: pink, colourless (1)

5 (a) It decreases. (1)

   (b) It increases. (1)

35. Strong and weak acids

1 answer D (1)

2 Nitric acid is fully/completely dissociated into ions in aqueous solution. (1)

3 (a) The reaction is reversible. (1)

   (b) It is partially dissociated into ions (in aqueous solution). (1)

4 The concentrated solution contains a greater amount of dissolved sodium hydroxide (1) in the same volume (1).

5 (a) At the same concentration/at 0.20 mol dm^{-3} (1) the pH of hydrochloric acid is lower than the pH of ethanoic acid (1).

   (b) Its pH increases by 1 (1) when the acid is diluted by a factor of 10/10 times (1).

      The pH increases as the acid is diluted, for 1 mark only.

(c) The concentration of hydrogen ions/H⁺ ions is the same. (1)

36. Bases and alkalis

1 answer B (1)

2 (a) $Na_2CO_3 + 2HNO_3 \rightarrow$
$2NaNO_3 + CO_2 + H_2O$

 1 mark for correct formulae, 1 mark for balancing

 (b) bubbles (1); powder disappears/dissolves (1)

 (c) (bubble the gas through) limewater (1) which turns milky/cloudy white (1)

3 (a) calcium chloride solution (1)
 (b) (i) hydrogen (1)
  (ii) **lighted** splint (ignites the gas) (1) with a (squeaky) pop (1)

4 (a) any substance that reacts with an acid (1) to form a salt and water only (1)
 (b) alkali (1)
 (c) zinc sulfate (1)

37. Neutralisation

1 Hydrogen ions/H⁺ ions from the acid (1) react with hydroxide ions/OH⁻ ions from the alkali (1) to form water (1). **H⁺(aq) + OH⁻ (aq) → H₂O(l) without reference to source of ions scores 2 marks.**

2 (a) CaO + 2HCl → CaCl₂ + H₂O

 1 mark for formulae, 1 mark for balancing

 (b) Ca(OH)₂ + 2HCl → CaCl₂ + 2H₂O

 1 mark for formulae, 1 mark for balancing

3 to make sure the readings/pH values are accurate (1)

4 points plotted accurately (± ½ square) (1); line of best fit (1); axes labelled using table headings (1)

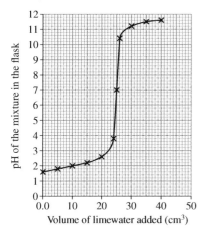

38. Salts from insoluble bases

1 (a) to react with **all** the acid (1) so that only a salt and water are left (with an excess of solid) (1)
 (b) to make the reaction happen faster/to increase the rate of reaction (1)
 (c) filtration/filtering (1)
 (d) crystallisation/evaporation (1)

2 (a) measuring cylinder/pipette/burette (1)
 (b) two improvements with reasons: 1 mark for improvement, 1 mark for its reason(s), e.g.

 • stir, to mix the reactants
 • add copper oxide one spatula at a time, to reduce waste

• warm the acid first, to make the reaction happen faster
• add copper oxide one spatula at a time until some is left over, to make sure that all the acid has reacted

 (c) Heat the evaporating basin over a hot water bath (1), allow to cool, and pour away excess water/dry crystals between paper/dry crystals in a warm oven (1).

39. Salts from soluble bases

1 answer C (1)

2 top label: burette; (1) bottom label: (conical) flask (1)

3 (a) hydrochloric acid (1)
 (b) (volumetric) pipette (1)
 (c) pink to colourless (1) **Both colours needed in the correct order for the mark.**
 (d) (i) to get an idea of how much acid must be added (1)
  (ii) run 1: 24.90; run 2: 24.40; run 3: 24.50 (1)
  (iii) (ignore 24.90);
  (24.40 + 24.50)/2 = 24.45 cm³

  1 mark for working out, 1 mark for answer

 (e) Repeat the titration without the indicator (1), add the mean titre volume of hydrochloric acid (to 25.0 cm³ of sodium hydroxide solution) (1).

40. Making insoluble salts

1 answer B (1)

2 answer D (1)

3 (a) calcium nitrate/calcium chloride (1) with sodium hydroxide/potassium hydroxide/ ammonium hydroxide (1)
 (b) Answer depends on the combination used in part (**a**), e.g. sodium nitrate/potassium nitrate/ammonium nitrate (if calcium nitrate used); sodium chloride/potassium chloride/ammonium chloride (if calcium chloride used). (1)

4 (a) Na₂CO₃(aq) + CaCl₂(aq) → 2NaCl(aq) + CaCO₃(s)

 1 mark for correct equation, 1 mark for correct state symbols

 (b) Dissolve sodium carbonate and calcium chloride in water then mix (1); filter to separate the precipitate of calcium carbonate (1); wash the precipitate with water (e.g. on the filter paper) (1); then dry in a warm oven/dry between pieces of filter paper/leave to dry (1).

5 Sulfuric acid contains sulfate *ions* (1) which react with lead ions (1) to form insoluble lead sulfate/an insoluble product (1).

41. Extended response – Making salts

*Answer could include the following points.

the titration:

• rinse a burette with dilute hydrochloric acid, then fill the burette with the acid
• measure 25 cm³ of sodium hydroxide solution using a pipette
• into a conical flask
• conical flask on a white tile
• add a few drops of phenolphthalein indicator/methyl orange indicator

• record the start reading on the burette
• add dilute hydrochloric acid from the burette to the sodium hydroxide solution
• swirl the flask
• add drop by drop near the end-point
• stop when colour changes/pink to colourless (phenolphthalein)/yellow to orange (methyl orange)
• record the end reading on the burette
• repeat the experiment
• until consistent/concordant results are obtained

using the titre:

• add 25 cm³ of sodium hydroxide to the flask
• do not add indicator
• add the titre/mean titre volume of dilute hydrochloric acid from the burette

producing the crystals:

• pour the mixture into an evaporating basin
• heat over a hot water bath
• until most of the water has evaporated
• allow to cool and pour away excess water
• dry crystals between filter paper/in a warm oven

42. Electrolysis

1 answer D (1)

2 An electrolyte is an ionic (1) compound in the molten/liquid state or dissolved in water (1).

3 MnO_4^- ions/manganate(VII) ions (1) move to the positively charged electrode/oppositely charged electrode (1).

4 cathode: zinc (1); anode: bromine (1) **not bromide**

5 (a) cathode (1)
 (b) Sodium ions are reduced (1) because they gain electrons (1).

6 (a) $Al^{3+} + 3e^- \rightarrow Al$ (1)
 (b) $2O^{2-} \rightarrow O_2 + 4e^-$ (2)

 1 mark for unbalanced equation

43. Electrolysing solutions

1 (a) answer D (1)
 (b) Some water molecules dissociate/ionise. (1)

  $H_2O \rightleftharpoons H^+ + OH^-$ (1)

 (c) $2Cl^- \rightarrow Cl_2 + 2e^-$ (2)

 1 mark for unbalanced equation

2 (a) Na^+, Cl^- (1) H^+, OH^- (1)
 (b) (i) chlorine (1)
  (ii) hydrogen (1)
 (c) hydroxide ions/OH⁻ ions are left over/in excess (1); alkalis in solution are a source of hydroxide ions/OH⁻ ions (1)

3 Hydroxide ions/OH⁻ ions from the water (1) are oxidised/lose electrons (1).

 equation for 2 marks:
 $4OH^- \rightarrow 2H_2O + O_2 + 4e^-$

4 Water is a covalent compound/a poor conductor of electricity/contains very few mobile ions (1); sulfuric acid increases the concentration of ions/increases the conductivity of the water (1).

44. Investigating electrolysis

1 (a) anode (1) because oxygen is formed from negatively charged ions/hydroxide ions (1)
 (b) $Cu \rightarrow Cu^{2+} + 2e^-$ (2)

 1 mark for unbalanced equation

127

2 (a) $Cu^{2+} + 2e^- \rightarrow Cu$ (2)

1 mark for unbalanced equation

(b) (i) time (1)
(ii) gain in mass by copper cathode (1)
(iii) (0.15 – 0.04)/(0.8 – 0.2) = 0.11/0.6 (1)
= 0.18 g/A

1 mark for correct answer, 1 mark for 2 significant figures

45. Extended response – Electrolysis

*Answer could include the following points.

copper chloride powder:

- its ions are not free to move
- in the solid state
- so there are no visible changes

copper chloride solution:

- its ions are free to move
- when dissolved in water/in solution
- brown solid is copper
- yellow-green gas is chlorine

electrode reactions:

- positively charged ions/copper ions attracted to negative electrode/cathode
- $Cu^{2+} + 2e^- \rightarrow Cu$
- negatively charged ions/chloride ions attracted to positive electrode/anode
- $2Cl^- \rightarrow Cl_2 + 2e^-$
- overall reaction: $CuCl_2(aq) \rightarrow Cu(s) + Cl_2(g)$

46. The reactivity series

1 (a) answer D (1)
(b) two from the following, for 1 mark each: temperature (of water/acid); mass of metal; surface area of metal; amount/moles of metal

2 (a) hydrogen (1)
(b) $Mg + 2H_2O \rightarrow Mg(OH)_2 + H_2$

1 mark for correct formulae, 1 mark for balancing

(c) magnesium oxide (1)

3 (a) $Al_2O_3 + \mathbf{3}H_2SO_4 \rightarrow Al_2(SO_4)_3 + \mathbf{3}H_2O$ (1)
(b) $\mathbf{2}Al(s) + \mathbf{3}H_2SO_4(aq) \rightarrow Al_2(SO_4)_3(aq) + \mathbf{3}H_2(g)$

1 mark for correct formulae, 1 mark for balancing, 1 mark for state symbols

(c) At the start, the acid reacts with the aluminium oxide layer. (1) Once this has reacted/been removed, the acid can react with the aluminium itself. (1)

47. Metal displacement reactions

1 (a) Copper is more reactive than silver. (1)
(b) $\mathbf{Cu(s)} + 2AgNO_3\mathbf{(aq)} \rightarrow \mathbf{2Ag(s)} + Cu(NO_3)_2\mathbf{(aq)}$

1 mark for correct formulae, 1 mark for balancing, 1 mark for state symbols

2 (a) copper (1)
(b) A metal cannot displace itself. (1)
(c) magnesium > metal X > zinc > copper

1 mark for correct positions of magnesium and copper, 2 marks if all correct

3 Aluminium is more reactive than iron (1) because aluminium can displace iron from its compounds/from iron oxide (1).

48. Explaining metal reactivity

1 A cation is a **positively** charged ion. (1)

2 (a) Ca^{2+} (1)
(b) Two (1) electrons are lost from the outer shell (1).
(c) (i) potassium (1)
(ii) gold (1)
(d) copper/silver/gold (1)

3 (a) Zinc is more reactive than copper (1) because it loses electrons more easily (1).
(b) (i) $Mg(s) \rightarrow \mathbf{Mg^{2+}(aq) + 2e^-}$

1 mark for formulae, 1 mark for balancing

(ii) $\mathbf{2}H^+(aq) + \mathbf{2e^-} \rightarrow \mathbf{H_2(g)}$

1 mark for formulae, 1 mark for balancing

49. Metal ores

1 (a) answer B (1)
(b) Hydrogen is flammable/could explode. (1)

2 a rock or mineral that contains a metal/metal compound (1) in amounts high enough to make extraction worthwhile (1)

3 They are very unreactive (1) so they do not react with other elements/oxygen (1).

4 (a) $SnO_2 + 2C \rightarrow Sn + 2CO$

1 mark for correct formulae, 1 mark for balancing

(b) Tin oxide is reduced (1) because it loses oxygen (1).

5 (a) $4Na + O_2 \rightarrow 2Na_2O$

1 mark for correct formulae, 1 mark for balancing

(b) Copper is unreactive/low down on the reactivity series. (1)

6 (a) Ti^{4+} (1)
(b) Titanium ions are reduced (1) because they gain electrons (1).

50. Iron and aluminium

1 (a) sodium/calcium/magnesium (1)
(b) zinc/copper (1)

2 heat with carbon (1)

$Fe_2O_3 + 3C \rightarrow 2Fe + 3CO$ **or**
$2Fe_2O_3 + 3C \rightarrow 4Fe + 3CO_2$

1 mark for correct formulae, 1 mark for balancing

3 (a) The ions in the electrolyte must be free to move (1) so it can conduct electricity (1).
(b) reduces the temperature/amount of energy needed (1)
(c) at the anode: $2O^{2-} \rightarrow O_2 + 4e^-$

1 mark for correct formulae, 1 mark for balancing

at the cathode: $Al^{3+} + 3e^- \rightarrow Al$

1 mark for correct formulae, 1 mark for balancing

4 (Production of aluminium by) electrolysis uses a lot of electricity (1), which is very expensive/more expensive than using carbon (to extract iron) (1).

51. Biological metal extraction

1 (a) correct order, starting at the top of table: 3, 5, 2, 1, 4 (1)
(b) Energy could be used to heat buildings/homes/to produce electricity (1), which makes money for the company (1), **or** Energy could be used in the processing of copper (1), which means that the company will need less fuel/reduce its energy costs (1).
(c) slow process/a lot of land is needed/land could be used for food crops instead (1)

2 (a) The acid may damage rivers/streams/land/rocks/living things. (1)
(b) (i) $Fe(s) + CuSO_4(aq) \rightarrow FeSO_4(aq) + Cu(s)$

1 mark for correct formulae, 1 mark for balancing, 1 mark for state symbols

(ii) Iron is more reactive than copper/forms cations more readily than copper does. (1)
(iii) Copper is more expensive than iron, so a more valuable product is made. (1)

52. Recycling metals

1 (a) answer B (1)
(b) two of the following, for 1 mark each: dust produced; noisy; land used; wildlife loses habitat; extra traffic; landscape destroyed

2 (a) Most lead for recycling is found in batteries (1) so lead does not need to be sorted from scrap metal waste (1).
(b) two of the following, for 1 mark each: conserves metal ores/limited resources; less energy needed; fewer quarries needed/saves land/landscape; less noise/dust produced

3 (a) Steel and aluminium are much more abundant than tin in the Earth's crust (1); tin is much more valuable than steel or aluminium (1).
(b) If little metal is used each year it may not be worthwhile recycling the metal/the mass used tells you the total amount of money/energy saved. (1)

53. Life-cycle assessments

1 2, 1, 4, 3 (1)

2 (a) 240 g = 240/1000 = 0.240 kg (1); energy used = 0.240 × 16.5 = 3.96 MJ (1)
(b) difference in mass of a bottle = (240 – 190)/1000 = 0.050 kg (1); difference in CO_2 emissions = 0.050 × 1.2 = 0.06 kg (1)

3 (a) PVC: producing the material; wooden: transport and installation (1)
(b) The PVC frame because it uses less energy (1); 20% of the energy/five times less energy (1).
(c) Answer could include ideas such as PVC does not biodegrade/may give off harmful substances; wood is biodegradable/rots/releases carbon dioxide when it rots. (1)

54. Extended response – Reactivity of metals

*Answer could include the following points.

basic method:

- I would start with powdered copper, iron, zinc, copper oxide, iron oxide and zinc oxide.
- mix a spatula of a metal powder with a spatula of a metal oxide powder

- put the mixture in a steel lid
- heat strongly from below
- record observations
- repeat with a different combination of metal and metal oxide

expected results (in writing and/or as a table, as here):

	Copper oxide	Iron oxide	Zinc oxide
Copper	not done	no visible change	no visible change
Iron	reaction seen/ brown coating	not done	no visible change
Zinc	reaction seen/ brown coating	reaction seen/ black coating	not done

using the results:

- count the number of reactions seen for each metal
- zinc has two reactions; iron has one reaction; copper has no reactions
- order of reactivity (most reactive first): zinc, iron, copper

controlling risks:

- use tongs because substances/apparatus is hot
- wear eye protection to avoid contact with (hot) powders
- stand back/use a safety screen/fume cupboard to avoid breathing in escaping substances/to avoid skin contact with hot powders

55. Transition metals

1 answer C (1)

2 between groups 2 and 3 (1) in the central/ middle/centre part of the periodic table (1)

3 (a) They tell you the charge on the iron ion (1) because iron(II) hydroxide contains Fe^{2+} ions and iron(III) hydroxide contains Fe^{3+} ions (1).

   (b) Iron is a transition metal (and these form coloured compounds) (1); magnesium is in group 2 and aluminium is in group 3 (and these form white or colourless compounds) (1).

4 Iron is a catalyst (1); it is not part of the balanced equation (1) so it must be chemically unchanged at the end of the reaction (1).

5 (a) metal C (1)
   (b) metal B (1)

56. Rusting

1 (a) oxygen/air (1), water (1)
   (b) hydrated iron oxide/hydrated iron(III) oxide (1)

2 (a) The layer of oil stops air/oxygen (1) and water reaching the steel (1).
   (b) to improve their appearance (1); to improve their resistance to corrosion (1)

3 It stops air/oxygen/water reaching the titanium. (1)

4 (a) galvanisation (1)

   (b) (i) sacrificial protection (1)
      (ii) Zinc is more reactive than iron (1) so it oxidises/corrodes instead of the iron (1).

5 $Sn \rightarrow Sn^{4+} + 4e^-$

   1 mark for correct formulae, 1 mark for balancing

57. Alloys

1 answer C (1)

2 (a) magnalium (1)
   (b) In pure aluminium the layers of atoms can slide over each other easily (1), but magnesium atoms are larger/distort the layered structure, (1) so the layers cannot slide over each other so easily in the alloy (1).

3 Two from the following, for 1 mark each: it is unreactive; it does not corrode/tarnish; it is malleable/shaped easily; it is shiny

4 Pure iron rusts but stainless steel does not rust (1) so it is useful for sinks/cutlery/ dishwashers/washing machines (1).

5 Aluminium is most suitable because although copper conducts electricity better than aluminium does (1) aluminium is stronger (1) and its density is lower so the cables will be more lightweight (1). **Both metals have good corrosion resistance so this is not a factor for choosing one rather than the other.**

58. Extended response – Alloys and corrosion

*Answer could include the following points.

method:

- electrolyte of silver nitrate solution/ $AgNO_3(aq)$
- put the spoon and a piece of silver in the electrolyte
- use a d.c./direct current power supply
- connect the spoon to the negative terminal of the power supply
- connect the silver to the positive terminal of the power supply
- the spoon is the cathode
- the silver is the anode
- turn on the power supply
- allow time for the silver layer to form
- remove the spoon
- wash the electroplated spoon to remove electrolyte/silver nitrate solution

These points could be made using a suitably labelled or annotated diagram instead.

half equations:

- at the cathode: $Ag^+(aq) + e^- \rightarrow Ag(s)$
- at the anode: $Ag(s) \rightarrow Ag^+(aq) + e^-$

59. Accurate titrations

1 gradual change in colour/no sharp end-point (1)

2 (a) phenolphthalein/methyl orange/litmus (1)
   (b) Colour change matches the indicator given in part (**a**) for 1 mark:

   phenolphthalein: pink to colourless **not clear**; methyl orange: yellow to orange/ red; litmus: blue to red

3 I would use a pipette with a pipette filler. (1)

For accuracy, I would read at eye level/draw the liquid up to the line/bottom of meniscus on the line. (1)

4 (a) start reading: 0.80 cm³ (1); end-point reading: 25.25 cm³ (1)
   (b) (end-point reading – start reading), i.e. (25.25 – 0.80) = 24.45 cm³ (1)

5 (a) to make sure that acid reacts completely with the alkali (1)
   (b) to obtain an accurate end-point/to avoid going past the end-point (1)
   (c) to obtain an accurate reading/to avoid a parallax error (1)

60. Concentration calculations

1 (a) 0.5 dm³ (1)
   (b) 0.125 dm³ (1)
   (c) 0.025 dm³ (1)

2 (a) 0.10/0.25 = 0.40 mol dm⁻³ (1)
   (b) (0.40/250) × 1000 = 1.6 mol dm⁻³ (1)
   (c) (0.020/50) × 1000 = 0.40 mol dm⁻³ (1)

3 (a) 0.15 × 40 = 6.0 g dm⁻³ (1)
   (b) 0.050 × 170 = 8.5 g dm⁻³ (1)
   (c) 0.220 × 36.5 = 8.03 g dm⁻³ (1)

4 (a) 4.8/24 = 0.20 mol dm⁻³ (1)
   (b) 19/95 = 0.20 mol dm⁻³ (1)
   (c) 21.0/159.5 = 0.132 mol dm⁻³ (1)

61. Titration calculations

1 (a) 1st titration 22.30 cm³; 2nd titration 22.65 cm³; 3rd titration 22.40 cm³ (1)
   (b) Ignore 2nd titration (not concordant)

   Mean = (22.30 + 22.40)/2 cm³ (1)
   = 22.35 cm³ (1)

2 amount of NaOH = 0.100 × (25.00/1000)
   = **0.002 50** mol (1)

   1 : 1 ratio between NaOH and HCl, so amount of HCl = **0.002 50** mol (1)

   concentration of HCl = (**0.002 50**/24.50) × 1000
   = **0.102** mol dm⁻³ (1)

3 amount of HCl = 0.200 × (27.50/1000)
   = 0.005 50 mol (1)

   1 : 1 ratio between NaOH and HCl, so amount of NaOH = 0.005 50 mol (1)

   concentration of NaOH = (0.005 50/25.00) × 1000 = 0.220 mol dm⁻³ (1)

4 amount of NaOH = 0.400 × (25.00/1000)
   = 0.0100 mol (1)

   2 : 1 ratio between NaOH and H_2SO_4, so amount of H_2SO_4 = 0.0100/2 mol (1)
   = 0.005 00 mol (1)

   concentration of H_2SO_4 = (0.005 00/31.55) × 1000 = 0.158 mol dm⁻³ (1)

62. Percentage yield

1 answer B (1)

2 the mass of product calculated from the balanced equation/maximum mass of product for a given mass of limiting reactant (1)

3 (a) percentage yield = 100 × (actual yield/ theoretical yield) (1)

   = 100 × (3.0/4.0) = 75% (1)

   (b) The reaction might not be complete/go to completion (1), and some magnesium oxide could be lost during the experiment (1).

4   Missing values: A 90 (1); B 85 (1); C 35 (1); D 2.50 (1); E 5.00 (1); 11.3 (1)

63.   Atom economy

1   answer A (1)

2   total M_r of desired product = 101

total M_r of all products = 101 + 18 = 119 (1)

atom economy = *100* × 101/119 = 84.9% (1)

3   total A_r of desired product = (2 × 56) = 112

total M_r of all products = 112 + (3 × 28)
= 196 (1)

atom economy = 100 × 112/196 = 57.1% (1)

4   (a) M_r of ethanol = (2 × 12) + (6 × 1) +
(1 × 16) = 24 + 6 + 16 = 46 (1)

M_r of carbon dioxide = 12 + (2 × 16) = 44 (1)

total M_r of desired product = (2 × 46) = 92

total M_r of all products = 92 + (2 × 44)
= 180 (1)

atom economy = 100 × 92/180 = 51.1% (1)

(b) Sell the carbon dioxide for something useful, e.g. fizzy drinks/fire extinguishers. (1)

64.   Molar gas volume

1   answer B (1)

2   (a) volume of chlorine = 24 × 2.0 = **48** dm³ (1)

(b) 24 × 0.50 = 12 dm³ (1)

(c) 24 × 1.25 = 30 dm³ (1)

3   (a) amount of hydrogen
=120/24 0000 = **0.005** mol (1)

(b) 6000/24 000 = 0.25 mol (1)

(c) 360/24 000 = 0.015 mol (1)

4   (a) 400 × 6.5 = 2600 cm³ (2.60 dm³) (1)

(b) 400 × (4 + 5) = 3600 cm³ (3.60 dm³) (1)

65.   Gas calculations

1   (a) amount of Mg = 2.4/24 = **0.10** mol (1)

(b) (i) 0.10 mol (1)

(ii) mass of MgO = **0.10** × 40 = **4.0** g (1)

(c) (i) 0.10/2 = 0.05 mol (1)

(ii) 24 × 0.05 = 1.2 dm³ (1)

2   (a) 0.30/23 = 0.013 mol (1)

(b) (i) 0.013 mol (1)

(ii) 0.013 × 40 = 0.52 g (1)

(c) (i) 0.013/2 = 0.0065 mol (1)

(ii) 24 000 × 0.0065 = 156 cm³ (1)

3   amount of hydrogen = 1.2/24 = 0.050 mol (1)

amount of water = 0.050 mol (1)

mass of water = 0.050 × 18 = 0.90 g (1)

66.   Exam skills – Chemical calculations

1   (a) (i) M_r of BaO = 137 + 16 = 153 (1)

amount = (250 × 1000)/
153 = 1634 mol (1)

(ii) 1634/2 = 817 mol (1)

(iii) 24 × 817 = 19 600 dm³ (1) **(19 608 by calculation)**

(b) M_r of BaO = 153 and M_r of O_2 = 32

total M_r of all products =
(2 × 153) + 32 = 338 (1)

atom economy = 100 × (32/338) = 9.5% (1)

(c) (i) The reaction may be incomplete (at stage 1 and/or at stage 2)/some solid or gas may be lost when handled. (1)

(ii) percentage yield = 100 × (21.9/26.1)
= 83.9% (1)

(d) (i) 0.125/2.50 = 0.0500 mol dm⁻³ (1)

(ii) 171 × 0.0500 = 8.55 g dm⁻³ (1)

67.   The Haber process

1   (a) answer A (1)

(b) The reaction is reversible. (1)

2   (a) temperature 450°C (1); pressure 200 atmospheres (1)

(b) It is a catalyst (1); it makes the reaction happen faster (1).

3   (a) none/no visible change (1)

(b) (i) The rate of the forward and backward reactions is the same/equal (1) and they continue to happen (1).

(ii) They do not change/they remain constant. (1)

68.   More about equilibria

1   (a) The position of equilibrium moves to the right (1) in the direction of the fewest molecules of gas/because there are 3 mol of gas on the left of the equation but only 2 mol on the right (1).

(b) The position of equilibrium moves to the left (1) in the direction of the endothermic reaction/away from the exothermic reaction (1).

(c) The position of equilibrium moves to the right. (1)

(d) (i) no change (1)

(ii) increased (1)

2   (a) 200°C **and** 1000 atm (1)

(b) (i) 30% (1)

(ii) Lower temperatures give a greater yield (1) but the rate of reaction is too low (1).

Higher pressures give a greater yield/rate of reaction (1) but very high pressures are expensive/need stronger equipment/need more energy to maintain (1).

69.   Making fertilisers

1   1 mark for each correct row to 3 marks maximum (**NH_4NO_3 already completed**):

Fertiliser compound	Element required by plants		
	Potassium	Phosphorus	Nitrogen
NH_4NO_3			✓
$(NH_4)_2SO_4$			✓
K_3PO_4	✓	✓	
KNO_3	✓		✓

2   neutralisation (1)

3   (a) Titration lets you find the correct proportions of acid and alkali (1) to mix together so that the solution contains only salt and water (1).

(b) Heat the solution to evaporate (most of) the water (1); allow to cool so crystals form (1); pour away excess water/dry with filter paper/dry in a warm oven (1).

4   (a) natural gas/coal (1); water (1); air (1)

instead of natural gas/coal and water (for hydrogen); crude oil (1) followed by cracking (1)

(b) Industrial production is a continuous process (1) but laboratory production is a batch process (1).

70.   Fuel cells

1   (a) A chemical cell produces a voltage (1) until one of the reactants is used up (1).

(b) A fuel cell produces a voltage (1) for as long as it is supplied with fuel and oxygen/air (1).

2   (a) Air contains oxygen/it supplies oxygen (1) which reacts with the hydrogen/fuel (1).

(b) water (1)

3   $CH_3OH + 1\frac{1}{2}O_2 \rightarrow CO_2 + 2H_2O$

1 mark for correct formulae, 1 mark for balancing

4   (a) rechargeable chemical cell because there are many more charging points/electric sockets (1) so the distance between them is less/can recharge at home/can recharge at work or at home (1) **or** fuel cell because a car can carry a lot of fuel (1) and can be refuelled quickly/more quickly than a chemical cell can be recharged (1)

(b) The car does not need to store hydrogen in a tank/powders are solid so easier to store than hydrogen/water is a liquid so easier to store than hydrogen. (1) The car may have a greater range/need refuelling less often/easier or safer to refuel. (1)

71.   Extended response – Reversible reactions

*Answer could include the following points.

temperature:

- the forward reaction is endothermic
- the position of equilibrium moves to the right when the temperature is high/increased
- 950°C is a high temperature
- so the yield of hydrogen will be high
- and the rate of reaction/rate of attaining equilibrium will be high

pressure:

- there are more molecules/moles of gas on the right of the equation
- 2 molecules/moles on the left but 4 molecules/moles on the right
- the position of equilibrium moves to the left if the pressure is decreased
- but the rate of reaction decreases as the pressure decreases
- and the gases must be under pressure to move through the reactor
- so the pressure cannot be low/cannot be atmospheric pressure

catalyst:

- the catalyst does not alter the position of equilibrium
- but it increases the rate of reaction/rate of attaining equilibrium

conclusion:

- temperature chosen allows a high equilibrium yield of hydrogen and a high rate of reaction

- pressure chosen is likely to be a compromise between position of equilibrium and rate of reaction
- the catalyst allows a high rate of reaction
- the conditions allow an acceptable yield of hydrogen in an acceptable time/a compromise between higher rate or yield and higher energy costs

72. The alkali metals

1 answer C (1)

2 Their atoms all have one electron in their outer shell. (1)

3 (a) $2Na(s) + 2H_2O(l) \rightarrow 2NaOH(aq) + H_2(g)$

allow multiples or fractions, e.g.

$Na(s) + H_2O(l) \rightarrow NaOH(aq) + ½H_2(g)$

1 mark for correct formulae, 1 mark for balancing, 1 mark for state symbols

(b) The reaction is exothermic/energy is transferred to the surroundings by heating. (1) Sodium has a low melting point. (1)

(c) Lighted splint (1) ignites the gas with a pop (1).

4 They are very reactive/react with water/react with air (1); oil keeps water away/air away (1).

5 three of the following, for 1 mark each: fizzing/bubbling; metal melts/forms a ball; metal floats; metal moves around; sparks produced; lilac flame; metal disappears/dissolves/explodes at the end

6 Going down the group, the size of the atoms increases (1); outer electron gets further from the nucleus/becomes more shielded/Li 2.1, Na 2.8.1, K 2.8.8.1 (1); attraction between outer electron and nucleus decreases/outer electron lost more easily (1).

73. The halogens

1 answer B (1)

2 Their atoms all have seven electrons in their outer shell. (1)

3 chlorine: yellow-green (1) gas (1); bromine: red-brown (1) liquid (1)

4 Density increases down the group (1); answer in the range 6000–7000 kg/m³ (1).

5 (a) covalent (1)

(b) There are intermolecular forces/forces between molecules (1); these are weak/need little energy to overcome (1).

(c) Melting points increase (1) because the intermolecular forces become stronger (1).

74. Reactions of halogens

1 (a) $H_2 + F_2 \rightarrow 2HF$

1 mark for correct formulae, 1 mark for balancing

(b) answer C (1)

(c) Bromine is less reactive than chlorine (and fluorine) (1) so more energy must be transferred to start the reaction/bromine gains an electron less readily (1).

2 (a) $2Na(s) + Cl_2(g) \rightarrow 2NaCl(s)$

1 mark for correct formulae, 1 mark for balancing, 1 mark for state symbols

(b) $2Fe + 3Br_2 \rightarrow 2FeBr_3$

1 mark for correct formulae, 1 mark for balancing

(c) (i) iron(II) Fe^{2+} (1); iodide I^- (1)

(ii) $Fe + I_2 \rightarrow FeI_2$

1 mark for correct formulae, 1 mark for balancing

3 Fluorine atoms are smaller than chlorine atoms (1); outer shell is closer to the nucleus/less shielded/F 2.7, Cl 2.8.7 (1); greater attraction between outer electrons/shell and nucleus/outer electron gained more easily (1).

75. Halogen displacement reactions

1 answer D (1)

2 (a) The order of reactivity, starting with the most reactive, is chlorine, bromine, iodine (1) because chlorine displaces bromine from bromide and iodine from iodide (1) but bromine only displaces iodine from iodide. Iodine cannot displace chlorine or bromine. (1)

(b) A halogen cannot displace itself (so no reaction will be seen). (1)

(c) Iodine will displace astatine because it is above astatine (1) so iodine is more reactive than astatine (1).

3 (a) $F_2(g) + 2I^-(aq) \rightarrow 2F^-(aq) + I_2(aq)$;

1 mark for correct formulae, 1 mark for balancing

(b) (i) Iodide/I^- ions are oxidised (1) because they lose electrons (1).

(ii) Fluorine/F_2 is reduced (1) because it gains electrons (1).

76. The noble gases

1 answer A (1)

2 Helium has a low density so the balloon will rise in air (1); helium is inert so it will not catch fire (1).

3 Their outer shells are full/complete. (1)

4 (a) helium (1)

(b) Melting point increases down the group (1); answer in the range −40°C to −20°C (1).

5 (a) (i) 2.8 (1)

(ii) 2.8.8 (1)

(b) The outer shells of their atoms are full/complete (1) so they have no tendency to gain/lose/share electrons (1).

77. Extended response – Groups

*Answer could include the following points.

reaction:

- caesium atoms transfer electrons
- from their outer shell
- to the outer shell of fluorine atoms
- each caesium atom loses one electron
- to form a Cs^+ ion
- each fluorine atom gains one electron
- to form an F^- ion
- oppositely charged ions/Cs^+ ions and F^- ions attract each other
- ionic bonds form

reduction and oxidation:

- caesium is oxidised
- caesium atoms lose electrons
- $Cs \rightarrow Cs^+ + e^-$
- fluorine is reduced
- fluorine molecules gain electrons

- $F_2 + 2e^- \rightarrow 2F^-$

vigour of reaction:

- reactivity increases down group 1/Cs loses its electrons more easily (than Li, Na, K, Rb)
- reactivity decreases down group 7/F gains electrons more easily (than any other group 7 element)
- caesium and fluorine are most reactive/very reactive

78. Rates of reaction

1 answer B (1)

2 The particles must collide (1); the collision must have enough energy/the activation energy (1).

3 (a) a substance that speeds up a reaction without altering the products (1) and is unchanged chemically (1) and in mass (1) (at the end of the reaction)

(b) provides an alternative pathway (1) with a lower activation energy (1)

(c) (i) enzyme (1)

(ii) making alcoholic drinks/wine/beer (1)

4 The powder has a larger **surface area to volume ratio** (1) so there are more frequent collisions between reactant particles (1) **not 'there are more collisions'**.

5 There are more frequent collisions between reactant particles (1); the particles/collisions have more energy (1), so a greater proportion of collisions are successful/have the activation energy or more (1).

79. Investigating rates

1 (a) Sodium chloride solution and water are both clear and colourless (1) so you could not tell that they are being produced (1).

(b) (i) gas syringe/upturned burette of water/upturned measuring cylinder of water (1)

(ii) The sulfur dioxide will dissolve in the water (1) so most will not escape/the volume measurement will be incorrect/inaccurate (1).

2 (a) water is added to make all the total volumes 50 cm³ (1)

(b) 8 (1), 24, 40 (1)

(c) As the concentration increases the rate increases/rate is proportional to concentration. (1)

but

Rate is directly proportional to the concentration. (2)

80. Exam skills – Rates of reaction

1 (a) all points plotted correctly ± ½ square (2); **1 mark if one error**

single line of best fit passing through all the points (1)

Do not use a ruler to join the points (apart from the last two) because a curve is required here.

(b) The mass does not change any more/the line becomes horizontal. (1) **not 'straight'**

(c) line drawn to the left of the original line (1) becoming horizontal at 0.96 g (1)

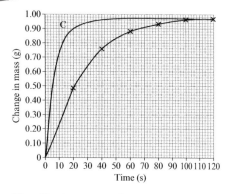

81. Heat energy changes

1   answer C (1)

2   In an exothermic change or reaction, heat energy is given out (1) but in an endothermic change or reaction, heat energy is taken in (1).

3   (a) endothermic (1)

    (b) acid-alkali neutralisation (1); aqueous displacement (1)

4   (a) $Mg(s) + 2HCl(aq) \rightarrow MgCl_2(aq) + H_2(g)$

    1 mark for correct formulae, 1 mark for balancing, 1 mark for state symbols

    (b) Measure the temperature of the acid before and after adding magnesium (1) using a thermometer (1) and the temperature should increase (1).

    (c) More heat energy is released (1) forming bonds in the products (1) than is needed to break bonds in the reactants (1).

82. Reaction profiles

1   Reactants have more stored energy than products/products have less stored energy than reactants (1); difference in energies shows that heat energy is given out (1).

2   (a) diagram completed with upwards arch between reactants and product lines (1); activation energy correctly identified (1)

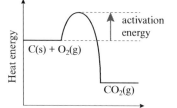

    (b) the minimum amount of energy needed to start a reaction (1)

3   diagram complete with reactant line below products line (1); upward arch between reactant and products lines (1); activation energy correctly identified (1); overall energy change correctly identified (1)

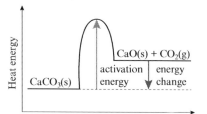

83. Calculating energy changes

1   (a) $(1 \times 436) + (1 \times 243) = 436 + 243$
       $= 679$ kJ mol^{-1} (1)

    (b) $(2 \times 432) = 864$ kJ mol^{-1} (1)

    (c) energy change = (energy in) – (energy out)
       $= 679 - 864$ kJ mol^{-1} (1)
       $= -185$ kJ mol^{-1} (1)

    (d) exothermic (1) because the energy change is negative/more energy is given out than is taken in (1)

2   energy in $= (1 \times 945) + (3 \times 436)$
       $= 945 + 1308$
       $= 2253$ kJ mol^{-1} (1)

    energy out $= (6 \times 391) = 2346$ kJ mol^{-1} (1)

    energy change $= 2253 - 2346$ kJ mol^{-1} (1)
       $= -93$ kJ mol^{-1} (1)

84. Crude oil

1   answer D (1)

2   A finite resource is no longer being made/is made extremely slowly (1); crude oil takes millions of years to form (1).

3   (a) C_6H_{14} (1)

    (b) They are compounds of hydrogen (1) and carbon only. (1)

4   (a) $C_8H_{18} + 12\frac{1}{2}O_2 \rightarrow 8CO_2 + 9H_2O$ or
       $2C_8H_{18} + 25O_2 \rightarrow 16CO_2 + 18H_2O$

    1 mark for correct formulae, 1 mark for balancing

    (b) Bubble gas through limewater, (1) which turns milky/cloudy white (1).

5   a starting material (1) for an industrial chemical process (1)

85. Fractional distillation

1   (a) answer D (1)

    (b) (i) bitumen (1)
       (ii) kerosene (1)

    (c) petrol (1); diesel oil (1)

2   alkanes (1)

3   The viscosity of fuel oil is too high for the fuel to flow easily (1) and it does not vaporise easily because its boiling point is too high (1).

4   There are weak forces (1) between molecules/intermolecular forces (1) so only a little energy needed to overcome/break these forces (1). **not covalent bonds**

5   Oil is evaporated (1) and passed into a column, which is hot at the bottom and cool at the top (1); hydrocarbons (rise) cool and condense at different heights (1), depending on boiling point/size of molecules/strength of intermolecular forces (1).

86. Alkanes

1   answer C (1)

2   (a) C_nH_{2n+2} (1)

    (b) (i) $C_{12}H_{26}$ (1)
       (ii) carbon dioxide (1); water (1)
       (iii) The alkanes react with oxygen/oxides are formed/carbon atoms and hydrogen atoms gain oxygen. (1)

3   (a) two from the following for 1 mark each: all contain carbon/hydrogen/oxygen/O–H group/covalent bonds/are simple molecules

    (b) differ by CH_2/one carbon atom **and** two hydrogen atoms (1)

87. Incomplete combustion

1   answer A (1)

2   (a) When breathed in, carbon monoxide combines with haemoglobin/red blood cells (1) so less oxygen can be carried/there is a lack of oxygen to cells (1).

    (b) They cause lung disease/bronchitis/make existing lung disease worse. (1)

3   any three from the following, for 1 mark each: nest restricts entry of oxygen; carbon monoxide will be produced; soot will be produced; carbon monoxide is toxic; soot causes breathing problems

4   (a) $C_3H_8 + 5O_2 \rightarrow 3CO_2 + 4H_2O$;
       1 mark for correct formulae, 1 mark for balancing

    (b) $C_3H_8 + 3\frac{1}{2}O_2 \rightarrow 4H_2O + C + CO + CO_2$
       1 mark for correct formulae, 1 mark for balancing

88. Acid rain

1   (a) $N_2 + 2O_2 \rightarrow 2NO_2$
       1 mark for correct formulae, 1 mark for balancing

    (b) Oxygen and nitrogen from the air (1) react together at the high temperatures inside the engine (1).

    (c) (i) sulfur (1)
       (ii) sulfur reacts with oxygen in the air (1)
       $S + O_2 \rightarrow SO_2$ (1)

2   $SO_2(g) + H_2O(l) \rightarrow H_2SO_3(aq)$
    1 mark for correct formulae and balancing, 1 mark for state symbols

3   (a) Marble/calcium carbonate reacts with acids/acidic rainwater (1) but granite does not (1).

    (b) damage to trees/plants/soil (1); makes lakes acidic/harms aquatic life (1)

89. Choosing fuels

1   It is being used up faster than it can form. (1)

2   (a) crude oil (1)

    (b) Petrol is used as a fuel for cars. Kerosene is used as a fuel for aircraft (1); diesel oil is used as a fuel for some cars/some trains (1).

3   (a) $2H_2 + O_2 \rightarrow 2H_2O$
       1 mark for correct formulae, 1 mark for balancing

    (b) carbon dioxide (1)

4   (a) volume needed $= 12\,000 \times (100/141.8)$
       $= 8460$ dm^3 (1)

    (b) volume needed $= 1.36 \times (100/47.3)$
       $= 2.88$ dm^3 (1)

    (c) (i) Hydrogen releases more energy per kg than petrol. (1)
       (ii) A much smaller volume of petrol is needed to release the same amount of energy as hydrogen/petrol is more energy dense. (1)

90. Cracking

1   answer D (1)

2   (a) alkene/unsaturated (1)

    (b) $C_{10}H_{22} \rightarrow C_8H_{18} + C_2H_4$
       1 mark for correct reactant, 1 mark for correct products

3 a reaction in which larger alkanes are broken down into smaller (more useful) alkanes/ smaller (more useful) saturated hydrocarbons (1) and smaller alkenes/unsaturated hydrocarbons (1)

4 (a) to make smaller molecules (1) that are in higher demand/more useful (1)
   (b) (from well B) because most of the alkanes have a small number of carbon atoms in their molecules (1) so are in demand/ more useful already (1)

91. Extended response – Fuels

*Answer could include the following points.

why incomplete combustion happens:
- incomplete combustion happens when there is insufficient oxygen/air
- this can happen if there is not enough ventilation, such as inside a tent
- not enough oxygen for complete combustion

products and their problems:
- carbon monoxide gas produced
- carbon monoxide is toxic
- combines with haemoglobin/red blood cells
- so less oxygen can be carried/there is a lack of oxygen to cells
- can cause unconsciousness/death
- carbon particles/soot produced
- cause lung disease/bronchitis/make existing lung disease worse
- cause blackening, e.g. of the bottom of the kettle/the inside of the tent
- balance equation, e.g. $C_3H_8 + 3O_2 \rightarrow 4H_2O + 2CO + C$; **many are possible**

other problems:
- less energy is released by incomplete combustion
- wastes camping gas/fuel
- takes longer to heat the water/to make the tea/to cook

92. The early atmosphere

1 answer B (1)

2 (a) nitrogen (1)
   (b) water vapour (in the atmosphere) (1) condensed (and fell as rain) (1)
   (c) carbon dioxide dissolved (1) in the oceans/water (1)

3 A **glowing** splint (1) relights (1).

4 The growth of primitive plants used carbon dioxide (1) and released oxygen (1) via photosynthesis (1).

5 They use different evidence/draw different conclusions from the same evidence/ study different parts of the Earth/no direct measurements are possible/no humans were on Earth at the time. (1)

93. Greenhouse effect

1 (a) methane (1)
   (b) (i) Fossil fuels contain hydrocarbons/ carbon, (1) which react with oxygen in the air to produce carbon dioxide (1).
      (ii) increasing use of fossil fuels (1) so carbon dioxide is released faster (1) than it can be removed (e.g. by photosynthesis, dissolving in the oceans) (1)

2 Various gases in the atmosphere, such as carbon dioxide, absorb heat radiated from the Earth (1) and then release energy/heat energy (in all directions) (1) which keeps the Earth warm (1).

3 (a) The measurements could not be taken directly/they are historical/their location may not be representative of the whole planet. (1)
   (b) As the carbon dioxide level increases, the global temperature increases (1); as the carbon dioxide level decreases, the global temperature decreases (1).
   (c) climate change/change in global weather patterns/ice caps melting/sea level rises/ loss of habitats (1)

94. Extended response – Atmospheric science

*Answer could include the following points.

greenhouse effect:
- carbon dioxide and some other gases in the atmosphere absorb heat energy
- radiated from the Earth
- then release energy
- which keeps the Earth warm

processes releasing carbon dioxide:
- burning fossil fuels
- respiration
- volcanic activity

processes absorbing carbon dioxide:
- dissolving in seawater
- photosynthesis

discussing the data:
- as the concentration of carbon dioxide rises
- the mean global temperature rises
- human activity, e.g. burning fossil fuels, could cause increase in temperature
- but there are some years when the temperature decreases
- carbon dioxide is also produced by other processes
- so it might not all be due to human activity
- there might be a common factor not shown in the graphs that is responsible for both changes

95. Tests for metal ions

1 1 mark for each correct flame colour, to 4 marks (**sodium already completed**):

Metal ion	calcium Ca^{2+}	copper Cu^{2+}	lithium Li^+	potassium K^+	sodium Na^+
Flame test colour	orange-red	blue-green	red	lilac	yellow

2 (a) Platinum does not produce its own flame colour/it does not melt in the flame/it is unreactive. (1)
   (b) It would be difficult to see the flame test colour/the flame may not be hot enough. (1)

3 (a) (i) blue (1)
      (ii) $Cu^{2+}(aq) + 2OH^-(aq) \rightarrow Cu(OH)_2(s)$

1 mark for balancing, 1 mark for state symbols
   (b) Iron(II) sulfate gives a green precipitate (1); iron(III) sulfate gives a brown precipitate (1).
   (c) Add more sodium hydroxide solution/ an excess of sodium hydroxide solution (1); only aluminium hydroxide dissolves/ forms a colourless solution (1).

96. More tests for ions

1 (a) 1 mark for each correct flame colour, to 2 marks (**AgCl already completed**):

Silver halide	AgCl	AgBr	AgI
Precipitate colour	white	cream	yellow

   (b) Hydrochloric acid contains chloride ions (1), which form a white precipitate/ precipitate of silver chloride/give a false-positive result for chloride ions (1).

2 (a) bubbles of gas produced (1)
   (b) Pass the gas through limewater (1), which should turn milky/cloudy white (1).

3 (a) White precipitate (of barium sulfate) forms. (1)
   (b) to react with carbonate ions/remove carbonate ions (1), which also give a white precipitate in the test (1)

4 (a) ammonia (1) **not 'ammonium'**
   (b) **damp** red litmus paper (1) turns blue (1) **or**
      exposed to hydrogen chloride fumes (from concentrated hydrochloric acid) (1) forms a white smoke (1)

97. Instrumental methods

1 improved sensitivity (1); improved accuracy (1); increased speed (1)

2 (a) (i) The lithium spectrum has two lines (1) that are not present in the mix spectrum (1).
      (ii) Na^+ (1); K^+ (1)
   (b) Obtain the reference spectra for different ions, then compare them with the spectrum from the unknown solution (1); if the lines match, the ion must be the same (1).

3 0.045 mol dm^{-3} (1)

98. Extended response – Tests for ions

*Answer could include the following points.

test for carbonate ions:
- add dilute acid to each sample
- lithium carbonate is the only one to produce bubbles
- confirm that bubbles are carbon dioxide using limewater
- limewater turns milky/cloudy white

test for sulfate ions:
- dissolve a little of each substance in water
- add a few drops of hydrochloric acid
- to prevent carbonate ions giving a false-positive result
- lithium carbonate solution should give brief bubbling
- add a few drops of barium chloride solution

- white precipitate forms with ammonium sulfate solution, sodium sulfate solution, aluminium sulfate solution

flame tests:

- carry out a flame test on each solid
- lithium carbonate gives a red flame
- sodium sulfate gives a yellow flame

hydroxide precipitate tests:

- dissolve a little of each substance in water
- add a few drops of dilute sodium hydroxide solution
- a white precipitate forms with aluminium sulfate solution
- this redissolves/disappears to form a colourless solution on adding excess sodium hydroxide solution

test for ammonium ions:

- add a few drops of dilute sodium hydroxide solution to each solid/each solution
- warm gently
- ammonium sulfate releases ammonia gas
- which turns damp red litmus paper blue

There are several possible sequences of tests to distinguish between the substances. Depending on your choice, you may not need to mention all the tests in your answer.

99. More about alkanes

1   (a) It is a compound of hydrogen and carbon (1) only (1).
    (b) Propane does not contain C=C bonds/ carbon–carbon double bonds (1); it contains only C–C bonds/carbon–carbon single bonds (1).

2   name: methane (1); molecular formula: C_2H_6 (1); structure (1):

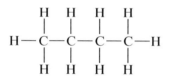

3   (a) carbon dioxide (1) and water (1)
    (b) $C_5H_{12} + 8O_2 \rightarrow 5CO_2 + 6H_2O$

    1 mark for correct formulae, 1 mark for balancing

    (c) $C_{16}H_{34}$ (1)

100. Alkenes

1   It is a compound of hydrogen and carbon (1) only (1) that contains the functional group C=C/carbon–carbon double bonds (1).

2   molecular formula: C_4H_8 (1); structure (1):

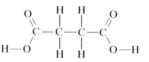

    The H atom on the C–H group can be down as shown here, or up.

3   (a) $C_3H_6 + 4\frac{1}{2}O_2 \rightarrow 3CO_2 + 3H_2O$

    1 mark for correct formulae, 1 mark for balancing

    (b) $C_{18}H_{36}$ (1)

4   Add bromine water/bromine (and shake). (1) No colour change/stays orange with hexane (1); turns from orange to colourless with hexene (1).

101. Addition polymers

1   a substance of high average relative molecular mass/formula mass (1) made up of small repeating units (1)

2   (a) addition polymerisation (1)
    (b) They have a C=C bond/carbon–carbon double bond. (1)
    (c) poly(ethene) (1)

3   Structure of propene (1):

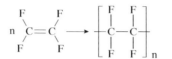

4   One of the bonds in the C=C bond in the monomer breaks (1); new C–C bonds form between molecules/molecules join together to form the polymer (1); equation given/repeating unit drawn (1).

5   two from the following for 1 mark each: PVC is a poor conductor of electricity/an insulator so the cable can be touched without getting an electric shock; PVC is tough so it protects the cable from damage; PVC is flexible so the cable can be bent

102. Condensation polymers

1   (a) O–H circled at either (or both) ends (1)
    (b) structure of butanedioic acid (2), e.g.

    Functional groups may be shown the other way up.

    1 mark if a covalent bond is not shown

    (c) (i) condensation polymer/polyester (1)
        (ii) water (1)

2   (a) O=C–O circled (1)
    (b) It contains many ester links/ester groups. (1)
    (c) A molecule of water (1) forms each time an ester link/ester group forms (1).

103. Biological polymers

1   condensation polymerisation (1)

2   (a) four (1)
    (b) nucleotides (1)

3   (a) amino acids (1)
    (b) H–N–H circled (1) and O=C–O–H circled (1)

4   (a) (i) CH_2O (1)
        (ii) It contains atoms of carbon, hydrogen and oxygen. (1)
        (iii) sugars/simple sugars/ monosaccharides (1)
    (b) starch/glycogen (1)

104. Polymer problems

1   (a) can be broken down/decomposed (1) by living organisms/bacteria/microbes (1)
    (b) (i) hole in the ground, e.g. disused quarry (1) where waste is dumped and then covered over (1)

    (ii) The polymers do not break down (1) so the landfill sites fill up/become full. (1)

2   (a) two from the following, for 1 mark each: volume/amount of waste is reduced; landfill sites do not fill up so quickly; energy released can be used, e.g. for heating or making electricity
    (b) harmful gases released (1); carbon dioxide is a greenhouse gas/hydrogen chloride is acidic (1)

3   (a) crude oil is conserved/less is used (1) because smaller amounts of new polymer are needed (1)
    (b) The different polymers will need to be sorted from each other. (1)

4   (a) The microbeads are very small (1) so they are not captured by the filters (1).
    (b) Living organisms swallow the microbeads (1) and the microbeads will not break down unless they are biodegradable (1).

105. Extended response – Hydrocarbons and polymers

*Answer could include the following points.

making poly(ethene):

- addition polymerisation
- ethene monomer needed
- one of the bonds in the C=C bond breaks
- new C–C bond forms between monomers
- ethene molecules join together to form poly(ethene)
- equation using structures, e.g.

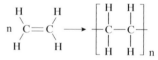

making PET:

- condensation polymerisation
- benzene-1,4-dicarboxylic acid **and** ethane-1,2-diol needed
- carboxylic acid group reacts with alcohol group
- benzene-1,4-dicarboxylic acid has two carboxylic acid groups
- ethane-1,2-diol has two alcohol groups
- ester link formed
- water molecule formed
- one water molecule formed for each ester link formed
- equation using structures of carbon compounds, e.g.

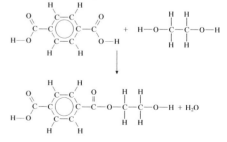

106. Alcohols

1   (a) 1 mark for each correctly completed box, for a total of 4 marks, e.g.

Name of alcohol	Formula	Structure
methanol	CH_3OH	
ethanol	C_2H_5OH	H—C—C—O—H (with H atoms)
propanol/ propan-1-ol	C_3H_7OH	

(b) O–H circled (1)

(c) They contain the same functional group/ the –OH group (1); the formula differs by CH_2 from one compound to the next (1).

2 (a) **1** bubbling/fizzing (1)

2 sodium dissolves/clear solution formed (1)

(b) (i) butanoic acid (1); water (1)

(ii) $C_4H_9OH + 2[O] \rightarrow$
$C_3H_7COOH + H_2O$

1 mark for correct formulae, 1 mark for balancing

107. Making ethanol

1 (a) ethanol **and** carbon dioxide (1)

(b) The yeast provide enzymes (1) needed to catalyse the fermentation reaction (1).

(c) (i) There would be no ethanol/carbon dioxide/products at 60°C (1).

(ii) The enzymes are denatured/damaged (1) so no fermentation happens (1).

2 (a) Their boiling points differ. (1)

(b) Heat the dilute solution of ethanol using a Bunsen burner/electric heater (1); ethanol boils first/has a lower boiling point than water (1); ethanol vapour goes into the condenser (1); the vapour is cooled and condensed to form a liquid (1).

108. Carboxylic acids

1 named indicator (1) with appropriate colour (1), e.g. universal indicator – yellow/orange; phenolphthalein – colourless; methyl orange – orange/red; litmus – red

2 (a) bubbles given off (1); sodium carbonate disappears/dissolves (1)

(b) hydrogen (1)

3 (a) O=C–O–H circled (1)

(b) HCOOH (1)

(c) correct structure of propanoic acid with all covalent bonds shown (1)

H—C—C—C (structure of propanoic acid with O=C and O—H)

4 (a) oxidation (1) because ethanol gains oxygen (1)

(b) methanol (1)

109. Investigating combustion

1 (a) change for 1 mark, with reason for 1 mark, e.g. use a shorter thermometer/ clamp the thermometer to stop it falling over/to reduce the chance of it being broken

(b) Alcohols are flammable. (1) The fuel in the burner could be set alight/could spill. (1)

(c) The temperature change will be lower (1) than expected because less energy is released by incomplete combustion/the soot will insulate the bottom of the can (1).

(d) two of the following, for 1 mark each: volume of water; distance of wick/ flame to the can; size of flame; starting temperature of the water; change in temperature of the water/mass of fuel burned/heating time

2 (a) ethanol 24°C **and** butanol 29°C (1)

(b) ethanol: $(42 - 18)/0.40 = 60°C/g$

butanol: $(47 - 18)/0.43 = 67°C/g$ (1)

so butanol produces the greatest change per gram of fuel (1)

110. Nanoparticles

1 answer B (1)

2 (a) $6 \times 10 \times 10$ (1)
$= 600 \text{ mm}^2$ (1)

(b) $10 \times 10 \times 10$ (1)
$= 1000 \text{ mm}^3$ (1)

(c) $600/1000 = 0.6$ or $0.6{:}1$ (1)

3 (a) Nanoparticles are too small to be seen (1) but still protect against ultraviolet light (1).

(b) may be absorbed through broken skin/ swallowed (1); small enough to enter cells in the body/may catalyse harmful reactions/may cause harm to health (1)

(c) Nanoparticles have a very large surface area to volume ratio (1) so reactant particles collide more frequently with the catalyst (1).

111. Bulk materials

1 answer D (1)

2 (a) It has the highest electrical conductivity (of the four metals) (1) so it will conduct electricity very well (1).

(b) chromium (1) because it is the hardest (1) and its melting point is very high/highest (1)

3 (a) two or more materials combined each with different properties/contrasting properties (1) to make a material with improved properties/better properties than the individual materials (1)

(b) glass is brittle (1); the polymer stops pieces of glass hitting the passengers in an accident/the composite material is tougher than glass alone (1)

112. Extended response – Materials

*Answer could include the following points.

FRR:

- cheapest material/about 20 times cheaper than CRP
- about 14 times weaker than CRP
- almost as strong as fibreglass
- slightly stiffer than fibreglass
- about 17 times less stiff than CRP
- low/lowest brittleness
- can be coloured (similar to fibreglass)
- can be pressed into shape/does not have to be built up in layers

fibreglass:

- twice the cost of FRR
- more than 10 times cheaper than CRP

- about 12 times weaker than CRP
- slightly stronger than FRR
- slightly less stiff than FRR
- 25 times less stiff than CRP
- less brittle than CRP
- more brittle than FRR
- can be coloured (similar to FRR)
- must be built up in layers/cannot be pressed into shape

CRP:

- most expensive
- expensive/20 times cost of FRR/10 times cost of fibreglass
- strongest material
- about 14 times stronger than FRR
- about 12 times stronger than fibreglass
- stiffest material
- about 17 times stiffer than FRR
- 25 times stiffer than fibreglass
- most brittle material
- black/cannot be coloured (unlike FRR and fibreglass)
- must be built up in layers/cannot be pressed into shape

conclusion, for example:

- FRR is best because it is the cheapest, almost as strong as fibreglass, does not shatter easily, can be pressed into shape (similar to steel) and can be coloured so does not need painting.
- Fibreglass is best because it is almost as cheap as FRR and has similar properties, but is stronger than FRR and much less likely to shatter than CRP.
- CRP is best because, although it is much more expensive than the other two materials, it is much stronger so less may need to be used to make the body panels.

113. Timed Test 1

1 (a) (i) answer B (1)

(ii) answer D (1)

(b) (i) They contain the same number of protons (1), 10 protons (1), but different numbers of neutrons (1), 10 or 12 neutrons (1).

(ii) $(90.5 \times 20) + (9.5 \times 22) = 2019$ (1)
$2019/100 = 20.19$ (1)
$= 20.2$ (1)

2 (a) similarity for 1 mark, e.g. elements in groups/periods; elements in a group have similar properties.

difference for 1 mark, e.g. elements in Mendeleev's table are arranged in order of relative atomic mass/elements in modern table arranged in order of atomic number; Mendeleev's table had fewer elements/gaps/no group 0 elements.

(b) completed diagram with two crosses on first circle, eight crosses on second circle, five crosses on outer circle for 1 mark:

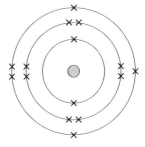

(c) Atoms of both elements have 7 electrons in their outer shell. (1) **Or** 2.7 and 2.8.7 with link made to number of electrons in outer shell. (1)

(d) Magnesium atoms have three occupied shells (1); calcium atoms have four occupied shells (1). **Or** 2.8.2 and 2.8.8.2 (1); link made to number of occupied shells (1).

3 (a) answer C (1)

(b) 13 protons (1), 14 neutrons (1), 10 electrons (1)

(c) strong electrostatic forces of attraction/ strong ionic bonds (1) between oppositely charged ions (1) which need a lot of heat energy to break/overcome (1)

(d) (i) $(35/250) \times 1000$ (1)
= 140 g dm^{-3} (1)

(ii) $Al^{3+}(aq) + 3OH^-(aq) \to Al(OH)_3(s)$

1 mark for correct formulae, 1 mark for balancing, 1 mark for state symbols

4 (a) answer A (1)

(b) A pair of electrons (1) is shared between two atoms (1).

(c) dot-and-cross diagram with: two bonding pairs of electrons between carbon and each oxygen atom (1), two non-bonding pairs of electrons on each oxygen atom (1), e.g.

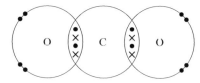

(d) (i) giant covalent structure/giant covalent lattice (1); many strong covalent bonds must be broken (1) (which needs a lot of energy)

(ii) Each carbon atom is bonded to three other carbon atoms (1) so there are free/delocalised electrons (1) that can move and carry an electric current (1).

5 (a) mass of magnesium: 1.21 g (1); mass of magnesium chloride: 4.79 g (1)

(b) $(4.79 - 1.21) = 3.58$ g (1)

(c) division of mass by A_r: Mg
$(1.21/24) = 0.0504$ **and** Cl
$(3.58/35.5) = 0.101$ (1)

simplest ratio: $1 : 2$ (1)

empirical formula: $MgCl_2$ (1)

(d) (i) amount of
$Al = (0.45/27) = 0.0167$ mol (1)

amount of $H_2 = (0.0167/2) \times 3$
$= 0.025$ mol (1)

volume of $H_2 = 0.025 \times 24$
$= 0.60$ dm^3 (1)

(ii) lighted splint (1) ignites gas with a pop (1)

6 (a) answer C (1)

(b) M_r of NaCl = 23.0 + 35.5 = 58.5 (1)

concentration of NaCl = 0.469 × 58.5 = 27.4 g dm^{-3} (1)

(c) (i) particles gain energy/move faster (1); particles move **much** further apart (1)

(ii) a lot of energy/fuel is needed to heat the seawater (1)

(iii) distilled water does not contain any dissolved salts (1) which would interfere/react with test substances (1)

(d) (i) removes **solid** particles/insoluble substances (1)

(ii) Chlorine is added (1) to kill harmful microbes/bacteria (which could cause disease) (1).

7 (a) answer B (1)

(b) precipitate of iron(III) hydroxide forms (1)

(c) (i) alkaline (1)

(ii) pH 1.70 (1)

(iii) Strong acid is fully dissociated into ions (1); weak acid is partially dissociated into ions (**do not allow 'not fully dissociated'**) (1).

(iv) $H^+ + OH^- \to H_2O$ (1)

*(d) Answer should include the following points:

reaction:

- dilute hydrochloric acid
- copper oxide/copper carbonate
- equation: $CuO + 2HCl \to CuCl_2 + H_2O/CuCO_3 + 2HCl \to CuCl_2 + H_2O + CO_2$
- warm the acid
- add portions of solid and stir
- continue until excess solid is left over

preparing the salt:

- filter to remove the excess solid
- heat gently in an evaporating basin/ leave in a warm place
- until crystals form
- dry crystals with paper/pour away excess liquid and leave to dry in an oven

8 (a) ionic compound (1) in the molten state/ dissolved in water (1)

(b) answer A (1)

(c) (i) Aluminium is more reactive than carbon. (1)

(ii) $2O^{2-} \to O_2 + 4e^-$ (1)

(d) $K^+ + e^- \to K$

1 mark for correct ion, 1 mark for the rest of the equation

(e) (i) to improve the appearance of a metal object (1); to improve the resistance to corrosion of a metal object (1)

(ii) anode – silver **and** cathode – steel cutlery (1); electrolyte: silver nitrate solution (1)

9 (a) answer D (1)

(b) (i) $2Fe_2O_3 + 3C \to 4Fe + 3CO_2$

1 mark for correct formulae, 1 mark for balancing

(ii) $100 \times (2.59 \times 10^5)/(2.95 \times 10^5)$ (1)
= 87.8% (1)

(c) M_r of SO_2 = 64.0

total relative mass of all products $= (2 \times 63.5) + 64.0 = 191$ (1)

atom economy $= 100 \times (2 \times 63.5)/191$ (1)
= 66.5% (1)

10 (a) answer B (1)

(b) answer B (1)

(c) The reaction is reversible. (1)

*(d) Answer could include the following points:

effect of higher temperatures in stage 1 (**or reverse arguments for lower temperatures**)

- increase the equilibrium yield of hydrogen
- decrease the time taken to reach equilibrium/increase rate of reaction
- increase energy costs
- but increase the rate of production

effect of higher pressures in stage 1 (**or reverse arguments for lower pressures**)

- decrease the equilibrium yield of hydrogen
- decrease the time taken to reach equilibrium/increase rate of reaction
- increase energy costs/cost of equipment needed
- but increase the rate of production

compromise conditions

- temperature is a compromise between yield/rate of production and costs
- pressure is a compromise between rate and yield
- pressure is sufficient to move gases through the reactor

effect of stage 2

- removes carbon monoxide so position of equilibrium in stage 1 moved to the right
- increases equilibrium yield of hydrogen in stage 1
- produces more hydrogen itself
- exothermic so it releases energy which could be used to heat gases for stage 1
- which reduces overall cost of the process

118. Timed Test 2

1 (a) answer A (1)

(b) (i) $2K(s) + 2H_2O(l) \to 2KOH(aq) + H_2(g)$

1 mark for formulae, 1 mark for balancing, 1 mark for state symbols

(ii) two from the following for 1 mark each: metal floats; (very rapid) fizzing/bubbling; lilac flame; sparks; explosion at the end

(c) (i) sodium: 2.8.1 (1); potassium: 2.8.8.1 (1)

(ii) Reactivity increases down group 1/ from lithium to potassium/as atoms get bigger (1); outer electron gets further from the nucleus/more shielded (1); weaker force of attraction between the nucleus and the outer electron/outer electron more easily lost (1).

2 (a) answer C (1)

(b) **Damp** blue litmus paper (1) turns (red then) white/is bleached (1).

*(c) Answer should include the following points:

- chlorine gains electrons
- chlorine is reduced
- to form chloride ions
- $Cl_2 + 2e^- \to 2Cl^-$
- iodide ions lose electrons
- iodide ions are oxidised
- to form iodine

- $2I^- \rightarrow I_2 + 2e^-$
- reduction and oxidation happen together/simultaneously

3 (a) answer D (1)

(b) amount of $CaCO_3 = 0.50/100 = 0.005$ mol (1)

amount of $HCl = 0.40 \times (50/1000) = 0.020$ mol (1)

(from equation) 1 mol of $CaCO_3$ reacts with 2 mol of HCl (1)

so $(2 \times 0.005) = 0.010$ mol of HCl needed but there is more than this/twice this (1)

(c) (i) Line drawn to the left of the original, starting at origin and with a similar shape (1); becomes horizontal at the same volume as the original (1).

(ii) At a higher temperature particles have more energy/move faster (1); collisions are more frequent/more collisions per unit time (1); more collisions are successful/have the activation energy or more (1).

4 (a) product line (labelled with formulae or as products) to the right and below the reactant line (labelled with formula or as reactant) (1); curve drawn on diagram (1); vertical arrow from height of reactant line to the top of the curve (labelled activation energy) (1). **See part (b) (i).**

(b) (i) curve drawn below the first and labelled X (1)

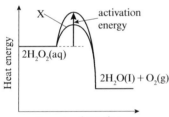

(ii) a substance that speeds up the rate of a reaction (without altering the products of the reaction) (1), being itself unchanged chemically (1) in mass at the end of the reaction (1)

(iii) provides an alternative reaction pathway/route (1), with a lower activation energy (1)

(c) The raw liver contains an enzyme (1) that catalyses the reaction/which is a biological catalyst (1).

5 (a) energy in to break bonds $= 612 + (4 \times 413) + (3 \times 498)$
$= 3758$ kJ/mol (1)

energy out when bonds form
$= (4 \times 805) + (4 \times 464) = 5076$ kJ/mol (1)

energy change $= 3758 - 5076$
$= -1318$ kJ/mol

1 mark for answer, 1 mark for negative sign

(b) More (heat) energy is released in forming bonds in the products (1) than is needed in breaking bonds in the reactants (1).

(c) two from the following for 1 mark each: same general formula; molecular formulae of neighbouring compounds differ by CH_2; show a gradual variation/trend in physical properties; have similar chemical properties

6 (a) answer B (1)

(b) (i) bitumen (1)

(ii) fuel oil (1)

(c) Crude oil takes millions of years to form/it is being made very slowly/is not being made any more. (1)

(d) Hydrocarbons (rise) cool and condense at different heights (as the column becomes cooler towards the top) (1); smaller molecules condense at greater heights (1), because they have weaker intermolecular forces (1), so their boiling point is lower (1). **Allow the reverse argument for the last three points.**

7 (a) answer D (1)

(b) The amount decreased because water vapour condensed to form oceans (1); carbon dioxide dissolved in the oceans (1); photosynthesis by plants used carbon dioxide (1).

(c) (i) **Glowing** splint (1) relights (1).

(ii) It is a greenhouse gas/it contributes to the greenhouse effect. (1) It absorbs heat radiated from the Earth (1), then releases energy (in all directions) which keeps the Earth warm/increases the temperature of the Earth (1).

(d) It produces acid rain (1), which corrodes metals/damages the structure of stonework, e.g. limestone or marble (1), which acidifies lakes/soils killing fish/trees (1).

8 (a) compound A: calcium (1) chloride (1)

compound B: copper/copper(II) (1) iodide (1)

(b) (i) iron(II)/Fe^{2+} (1) **not iron or iron(III)**

(ii) Iron(II) ions are oxidised (1) to iron(III) ions (1); the mixture also contains ammonium ions (1).

(iii) sulfate/SO_4^{2-} (1)

(iv) $Fe(NH_4)_2(SO_4)_2$ (2)

1 mark if correct ions but incorrect numbers of each

9 (a) C_3H_8 (1)

(b) CH_3 (1)

(c) $CH_3CH=CH_2$ (1)

(d) structure of but-2-ene (2), e.g.

$$H-\underset{\underset{H}{|}}{\overset{\overset{H}{|}}{C}}-\underset{\underset{H}{|}}{\overset{\overset{H}{|}}{C}}=\underset{}{\overset{\overset{H}{|}}{C}}-\underset{\underset{H}{|}}{\overset{\overset{H}{|}}{C}}-H$$

H atoms on the C=C atoms can be both up, both down, or one up one down.

If C=C is in the wrong place, 1 mark only.

(e) (i) $CH_2=CH_2 + Br_2 \rightarrow CH_2BrCH_2Br$ (1)

(ii) addition (1)

(f) Add bromine water to each substance: changes from orange–brown to colourless with ethene (1); no change/stays orange–brown with ethane (1).

1 mark maximum if orange-brown not mentioned

10 (a) structure of ethanol (1), e.g.

$$H-\underset{\underset{H}{|}}{\overset{\overset{H}{|}}{C}}-\underset{\underset{H}{|}}{\overset{\overset{H}{|}}{C}}-O-H$$

OH group must be shown as O–H

*(b) Answer could include the following points:

- dissolve sugars in water
- add yeast
- to provide enzymes
- needed for fermentation
- keep warm
- leave for a few days/weeks
- ethanol and carbon dioxide produced
- $C_6H_{12}O_6 \rightarrow 2CH_3CH_2OH + 2CO_2$
- filter/decant mixture
- use fractional distillation
- to separate ethanol from the mixture
- ethanol has a lower boiling point than water
- ethanol distils first

(c) Ethene is obtained from crude oil (1) which is a non-renewable resource/finite resource, but plant sugars (to make ethanol) are renewable (1).

(d) Nanoparticles have a large surface area to volume ratio (1); silver is a transition metal (1).

The Periodic Table of the Elements

Key

relative atomic mass
atomic symbol
name
atomic (proton) number

Example:

1
H
hydrogen
1

1	2											3	4	5	6	7	0
																	4 **He** helium 2
7 **Li** lithium 3	9 **Be** beryllium 4											11 **B** boron 5	12 **C** carbon 6	14 **N** nitrogen 7	16 **O** oxygen 8	19 **F** fluorine 9	20 **Ne** neon 10
23 **Na** sodium 11	24 **Mg** magnesium 12											27 **Al** aluminium 13	28 **Si** silicon 14	31 **P** phosphorus 15	32 **S** sulfur 16	35.5 **Cl** chlorine 17	40 **Ar** argon 18
39 **K** potassium 19	40 **Ca** calcium 20	45 **Sc** scandium 21	48 **Ti** titanium 22	51 **V** vanadium 23	52 **Cr** chromium 24	55 **Mn** manganese 25	56 **Fe** iron 26	59 **Co** cobalt 27	59 **Ni** nickel 28	63.5 **Cu** copper 29	65 **Zn** zinc 30	70 **Ga** gallium 31	73 **Ge** germanium 32	75 **As** arsenic 33	79 **Se** selenium 34	80 **Br** bromine 35	84 **Kr** krypton 36
85 **Rb** rubidium 37	88 **Sr** strontium 38	89 **Y** yttrium 39	91 **Zr** zirconium 40	93 **Nb** niobium 41	96 **Mo** molybdenum 42	[98] **Tc** technetium 43	101 **Ru** ruthenium 44	103 **Rh** rhodium 45	106 **Pd** palladium 46	108 **Ag** silver 47	112 **Cd** cadmium 48	115 **In** indium 49	119 **Sn** tin 50	122 **Sb** antimony 51	128 **Te** tellurium 52	127 **I** iodine 53	131 **Xe** xenon 54
133 **Cs** caesium 55	137 **Ba** barium 56	139 **La*** lanthanum 57	178 **Hf** hafnium 72	181 **Ta** tantalum 73	184 **W** tungsten 74	186 **Re** rhenium 75	190 **Os** osmium 76	192 **Ir** iridium 77	195 **Pt** platinum 78	197 **Au** gold 79	201 **Hg** mercury 80	204 **Tl** thallium 81	207 **Pb** lead 82	209 **Bi** bismuth 83	[209] **Po** polonium 84	[210] **At** astatine 85	[222] **Rn** radon 86
[223] **Fr** francium 87	[226] **Ra** radium 88	[227] **Ac*** actinium 89	[261] **Rf** rutherfordium 104	[262] **Db** dubnium 105	[266] **Sg** seaborgium 106	[264] **Bh** bohrium 107	[277] **Hs** hassium 108	[268] **Mt** meitnerium 109	[271] **Ds** darmstadtium 110	[272] **Rg** roentgenium 111							

Elements with atomic numbers 112–116 have been reported but not fully authenticated

*The lanthanoids (atomic numbers 58–71) and the actinoids (atomic numbers 90–103) have been omitted.

The relative atomic masses of copper and chlorine have been rounded to the nearest whole number.

Published by Pearson Education Limited, 80 Strand, London, WC2R 0RL.

www.pearsonschoolsandfecolleges.co.uk

Copies of official specifications for all Pearson qualifications may be found on the website: qualifications.pearson.com

Text and Illustrations © Pearson Education Limited 2017
Typeset and illustrations by Phoenix Photosetting
Illustrated by Techset Ltd
Cover illustration © Miriam Sturdee

The right of Nigel Saunders to be identified as author of this work has been asserted by him in accordance with the Copyright, Designs and Patents Act 1988.

First published 2016

19 18 17 16
10 9 8 7 6 5 4 3 2 1

British Library Cataloguing in Publication Data
A catalogue record for this book is available from the British Library

ISBN 978 1 292 13194 8

Acknowledgements
Content written by Ian Roberts and Damian Riddle is included with contributions by Roderick Stinton and Noyan Erdenizci.

The author and publisher would like to thank the following individuals and organisations for permission to reproduce photographs:

Alamy Images: Bruce Boulton.co.uk 91; **Pearson Education Ltd:** Oxford Designers & Illustrators Ltd 79, Trevor Clifford 109
All other images © Pearson Education

Some content has been reused from the following titles:
9781446902622 Revise Edexcel GCSE Science Revision Workbook Higher by Peter Ellis, Damian Riddle, Ian Roberts, Julia Salter
9781446902660 Revise Edexcel GCSE Additional Science Revision Workbook Higher by Peter Ellis, Damian Riddle, Ian Roberts
9781446902585 Revise Edexcel GCSE Science Extension Units Revision Workbook by Peter Ellis, Damian Riddle, Stephen Winrow-Campbell

Notes from the publisher
1. In order to ensure that this resource offers high-quality support for the associated Pearson qualification, it has been through a review process by the awarding body. This process confirms that this resource fully covers the teaching and learning content of the specification or part of a specification at which it is aimed. It also confirms that it demonstrates an appropriate balance between the development of subject skills, knowledge and understanding, in addition to preparation for assessment.

Endorsement does not cover any guidance on assessment activities or processes (e.g. practice questions or advice on how to answer assessment questions), included in the resource nor does it prescribe any particular approach to the teaching or delivery of a related course.

While the publishers have made every attempt to ensure that advice on the qualification and its assessment is accurate, the official specification and associated assessment guidance materials are the only authoritative source of information and should always be referred to for definitive guidance.

Pearson examiners have not contributed to any sections in this resource relevant to examination papers for which they have responsibility.

Examiners will not use endorsed resources as a source of material for any assessment set by Pearson.

Endorsement of a resource does not mean that the resource is required to achieve this Pearson qualification, nor does it mean that it is the only suitable material available to support the qualification, and any resource lists produced by the awarding body shall include this and other appropriate resources.

2. Pearson has robust editorial processes, including answer and fact checks, to ensure the accuracy of the content in this publication, and every effort is made to ensure this publication is free of errors. We are, however, only human, and occasionally errors do occur. Pearson is not liable for any misunderstandings that arise as a result of errors in this publication, but it is our priority to ensure that the content is accurate. If you spot an error, please do contact us at resourcescorrections@pearson.com so we can make sure it is corrected.

Notes